Keeper of Your Life

Actively Trusting Jesus Through Chronic Pain

Kelly J. Aalseth

ISBN 978-0-692-04224-3

All scriptures are from the NIV translation unless otherwise noted.

This book is dedicated to students of color who have modeled for me how to trust Jesus through generations of chronic pain. To the students in InterVarsity, Jesus for Revolutionaries, and IDEAS, thank you for bringing the presence of Jesus to those who've been hurting for a long time.

InterVarsity Christian Fellowship is vibrant campus ministry that establishes and advances witnessing communities of students and faculty. (intervarsity.org)

Jesus for Revolutionaries (J4R) is a movement of activists engaging issues of justice from a Biblical perspective. (jesus4revolutionaries.com)

IDEAS is a student group at UCLA that seeks to improve dreams, equality, and access for undocumented students. (ideasucla.weebly.com)

Thank you to my husband, Michael Lee Aalseth, for reminding me never to say never. And thank you to my copy editor, Sandy Joiner (a.k.a. Mom), the master at sentence diagramming and my life-long writing teacher.

Contents

I lift up my eyes to the hills—

from where will my help come?
My help comes from the Lord,
who made heaven and earth.

He will not let your foot be moved.
He who keeps you will not slumber.
He who keeps Israel
will neither slumber nor sleep.

The Lord is your keeper;
the Lord is your shade at your right hand.
The sun shall not strike you by day,
nor the moon by night.
The Lord will keep you from all evil;
he will keep your life.
The Lord will keep your going out and your coming in
from this time on and forevermore.

- Psalm 121 (NRSV)

Introduction

GET UP AND BE CARRIED

I was searching intently for ripe avocados in the grocery store when suddenly a stranger turned to me and said, "It seems you don't care about the most important part of your body." Come again? "Your Ugg boots," she said as she pointed to my feet. "You really ought to care about your feet more. Those shoes give you no support."

I looked at her in disbelief and what I really wanted to say was, "You are so right. My ugly running shoes are much better for my feet. That is why I wore them to an hour of physical therapy this morning, and through all of my work meetings, and during my mandatory walks and stretching routines, and while doing my breathing exercises and drinking my disgusting vitamin smoothies. Now I am at the grocery store so I can cook a meal that is free of gluten, dairy, soy, and sugar, while all of my friends are relaxing at home with their pizza. And as I mustered up all that was left of my energy to get here, I thought it would be nice to just this once feel like a normal human being and so I decided to wear my Uggs. Thank you for your concern."

Instead, I gave a small smile and turned back to my avocados.

If you have suffered through chronic pain, you know this experience. There are a million ideas out there about what you are supposed to do to manage pain and if you try to do them all perfectly, you are bound to wind up deflated. Managing any type of pain is fatiguing, but managing a pain that has been labeled as having no possible ending is just exhausting.

Three out of four Americans have either personally experienced chronic pain or have a close family member or friend who has,[1] and over 1.5 billion people worldwide suffer from chronic pain.[2]

I developed symptoms of fibromyalgia when I was 25. Fibromyalgia is "a chronic condition that causes widespread muscle pain (known as "myalgia") and extreme tenderness in many areas of the body." It affects 8% of people over the age of 20 in the U.S. and, though more prevalent in women, it affects people of all genders and ethnicities.[3]

Fibromyalgia affects everyone differently, but for me it has meant pain in my stomach, neck, back, legs, head, jaw, and feet on a continual but often alternating basis. I also have had related conditions such as irritable bowel syndrome (IBS), chronic fatigue syndrome (CFS), burning mouth syndrome (BMS), anxiety and depression.

While each of our experiences with chronic pain are distinct, we all share one thing in common: we are learning what it is like to suffer for a long time. Whether you are reading this book because of your own pain, or because you want to care for someone who is in pain, you are not alone in having to confront the realities that come along with that loaded little label, "chronic."

What are we to do with this diagnosis? How do we work to solve a problem when we have been told there will never be a solution? How do we motivate ourselves to keep trying the umpteen new things that could potentially help us when we have been told there is permanence to our condition? What is our role in looking for hope and healing and what simply requires us to wait for a miracle?

There is a story of a man who also shares in our experience of suffering for a long time. His story shapes the premise of this book. The story goes like this:

> *Some time later, Jesus went up to Jerusalem for one of the Jewish festivals. Now there is in Jerusalem near the Sheep Gate a pool, which in Aramaic is called Bethesda and which is surrounded by five covered colonnades. Here a great number of disabled people used to lie—the blind, the lame, the paralyzed. One who was there had been an invalid for thirty-eight years. When Jesus saw him lying there and learned that he had been in this condition for a long time, he asked him, "Do you want to get well?"*
>
> *"Sir," the invalid replied, "I have no one to help me into the pool when the water is stirred. While I*

am trying to get in, someone else goes down ahead of me."

Then Jesus said to him, "Get up! Pick up your mat and walk." At once the man was cured; he picked up his mat and walked.

- John 5:1-9

This man is so tired. Tired of seeing others get their prayers answered while nothing changes for him. Tired of asking for help—or thinking about asking for help. Tired of feeling powerless. Tired of being judged. Tired of feeling lonely. Tired of hoping. And so he sits every day, gazing at the pool in front of him and tracing the pattern of the five colonnades, knowing that nothing about them or the place he sits will ever change.

And it is in this place of tiredness, that Jesus shows up and has the audacity to tell him to get up and walk.

What is Jesus thinking? How is he any different from the woman in the grocery store who saw it her duty to add one more thing to my list of impossible things that I must do to cure myself? Is Jesus judging him for not doing anything to correct his chronic problem? Or is he empowering the man?

We are contradictory people. On one hand, we venerate self-empowerment. We love watching movies and reading stories about people who overcome challenges by willpower and self-discipline. We read Buzzfeed articles that say we can follow just ten steps and become the sexiest, healthiest, richest, and happiest people in the world. We are fascinated with research that suggests we can heal ourselves if we just reprogram our minds. We buy all kinds of products that are marketed as things that will help us gain control over our lives. We love the idea of being able to heal ourselves.

On the other hand, we are cynical people. We watch the news and feel skeptical that affecting any sort of change in this world is possible. We do not trust those who tell us how to live our lives and we are constantly on the lookout for ways we are being manipulated or deceived. We question the narrative that hard work will accomplish anything and are fatigued by the thought of delayed gratification.

And so we are left to believe that if we are not doing well, then we either need to work harder to find the right information that can lead us to curing ourselves, or we need to give up altogether because we have been duped into false hope.

But Jesus isn't interested in letting us stay paralyzed in our cynicism. Nor is he interested in offering us a self-help book so we can cure ourselves. Jesus empowers us to get ourselves up by teaching us how to be carried.

There is another story of a paralyzed man who is told by Jesus to get up and walk. (Mark 2:2-12) This man is no superhero. He is not likely to write the next Buzzfeed article about the ten steps to living a healthier life, or make it on the cover of Time magazine for his amazing abilities to overcome life obstacles. The story is not even about him at all. It is about his friends and their faith. When they hear that Jesus is in town and has a reputation of being a miraculous healer, they begin to carry their friend to Jesus. But because Jesus is so popular, they cannot get through the crowds to get into the house where Jesus is staying. So they do something ridiculous and dig a hole through the roof and lower the paralyzed man down to Jesus to be healed.

Healing for this man begins, not when he figures out how to manage his life perfectly, but when he allows himself to be carried. He vulnerably lets his friends, who are so determined to get him to Jesus, cause a messy and disruptive scene in front of the most respected people in town. He risks the potential for major disappointment by admitting that there is nothing in his own power that can change his condition, and by putting his hope in Jesus.

Jesus calls us out of our cynicism and into taking an active role in our healing, but that action is not based in an assumption that we can somehow think positively enough to produce a miracle or be self-disciplined enough to take control of our lives. It is an action that is founded in the belief that Jesus is the only one who can save us.

As I recently lay awake in the middle of the night, my breath quickening from the incessant and mysterious burning sensation in my feet, I used every coping skill I had learned from the last seven years of fighting chronic pain. I quoted scripture. I played music. I did breathing exercises. I stretched and put on oils. I took medication. I focused on gratitude. I prayed for everyone I knew who was also hurting. I reached out to my husband. I cried. I tried picturing Jesus. I even prayed in tongues.

While all of those skills are really great (some of which I advocate for throughout this book), they, in and of themselves, are not enough to take away the pain. I need something from outside myself, something supernatural to bring me relief and rest.

We cannot cure ourselves. No amount of inner drive, goal setting, therapy sessions, coping strategies or even eloquent prayer will be enough to overcome all the pain that comes to us. But that does not mean that resigning to defeat is our only answer.

The man in John 5 gazed every day at the pool of Bethesda, cynically aware that he would never be able to get himself close enough to that place of healing, and resigned to the fact that no one wanted to help him get there. But then his gaze was redirected to the person standing in front of him who was asking for his trust. He was able to get up and walk, not because of his own ability, but because he chose to put his trust in the only person powerful enough to make him do it.

Getting up and walking is not a matter of gaining enough

information and strategy. It is a matter of trust. It is about letting go of control long enough to let ourselves be carried. More than any coping skill, health regimen, or exercise challenge, learning to trust is the most difficult thing we can ever do. And Jesus stands in front of us, telling us that he is here to help us learn to do just that.

The following chapters are filled with practical suggestions of how to take an active role in trusting Jesus in the midst of chronic pain. You will discover Biblical stories, insights from my own experiences, as well as reflection questions to help you actively go to Jesus in the midst of your pain. You can read the chapters in any order, by yourself or with a study group. I pray as you read that you will hear Jesus' voice of empowerment helping you to get up and walk.

But do not read with the hope of finding the perfect formula to make you well. Read knowing that Jesus is compassionately looking right at you and wants to help you trust him to be the keeper of your life. He is the only one who has power to change anything in your situation and he is the one who will give you the courage you need to keep walking.

QUESTIONS FOR REFLECTION

- *What is your chronic pain? Are there other people you know who are experiencing chronic pain that you want to think about as you read this book?*
- *Do you lean towards wanting to cure yourself or wanting to give up in defeat? Where are you today on that spectrum?*
- *How do you feel about letting yourself be carried?*
- *How might Jesus be inviting you to take a more active role in going to him for grace and hope?*

The Rythmic Tune of Silent Suffering

One two three four one…
Breathe
Say it
I can't…two three four
Now
Now's your chance
Longer...one two three
Breathe
Ok
My eyes say it...four one two
Notice, please
Words
I can't...three four one
Waited
too long
Breathe
They notice
Shouldn't they?...two three four
Cry, please cry
Not coming
Almost
SPEAK
Ok
BREATHE…
"I hurt."

- Kelly Aalseth, 2016

Chapter 1

THE ART OF ASKING FOR HELP

I called up my friend, as a new flare of pain shot through my spine, and before I could even spit out the words, "I'm hurting," she said, "I'm coming," and drove an hour to come spend the day with me. My neighbor went to the store and bought some medication for me. Another two friends came over and spent a while praying for me. My second grade Sunday-School teacher pulled her network of intercessors together and they began to pray for me from afar. My brother quickly started researching helpful therapies for me. My sister talked me through how to pass off some of my work. My husband came home from work early, helped me fix dinner and made me laugh so hard that I was able to forget for a moment that I was in an exceptional amount of pain.

This kind of community does not just happen overnight. You do not just wake up one morning and suddenly have a whole group of friends and family who know exactly the right ways to help and encourage you when you go through pain. Building a team requires a great deal of effort and courage. It requires you to get up and learn the art of asking for help.

There is a lot working against us in learning this art. Social media makes it, on one hand, easier to ask for help.

You can tell thousands of people anything you want in about ten seconds: that you stubbed your toe or that you are on your deathbed. And, either way, you are certain to receive a lot of sympathy and probably even some "I'm praying for you"s. But the chances you will actually receive the help you desire is pretty slim.

Gender, culture and personality can also work against us. Some of us fight the stereotype of being "overly emotional" or "too sensitive" so we work hard to guard ourselves from that judgment. Others of us fear that if we do not show enough emotion we may not be taken seriously, so we over-share in order to get people to listen. Others of us have to fight the stereotype that asking for help is a sign of weakness and have trouble asking for help at all. Some of us feel fine publishing our lives for the world to see, but don't actually know how to build real intimacy. Others of us are better sharing with one or two close friends but constantly fear being a burden.

WHILE OUR OBSTACLES MAY BE SLIGHTLY DIFFERENT, WE ALL CAN FEEL CHALLENGED IN KNOWING EXACTLY HOW TO ASK FOR HELP

I was carpooling with my roommate one morning to a work meeting that was about an hour and a half away. I woke up with irritable bowel syndrome (IBS) pain and did not have enough time in the bathroom for the pain to subside before it was time to leave. Even though my roommate was one of my best friends, and very understanding of my health problems, I could not get myself to tell her I needed a little more time. I spent the entire car ride in silence, hoping that my silence would prompt her to read my mind and that somehow she would magically pull over for me to use the bathroom. But she did not read my mind, and the pain just kept escalating and my insides kept screaming.

I felt like the paralyzed man sitting at the pool of Bethesda: I knew that the only way I would find relief was if I asked for help, but I had no idea how to even begin to open my mouth.

There are other times where I am not allowed the luxury of being silent in my pain. When pain gets so high I can have panic attacks. I start to hyperventilate and because I do not retain enough CO2 to counter the high amount of oxygen I've inhaled, my arms and legs can start to lose control too. It is not dangerous, it just looks dramatic and loud. But even though my body is making it obvious that I am in pain, I still need to have courage to know how to ask for help. I know that I need someone to get me a brown paper bag and to ask me questions about what caused the anxiety that led to the panic attack, so that my breathing can slow. But when a friend or stranger is with me, wondering what they can do to help, it suddenly feels like climbing Mt.

Everest to articulate my specific needs.

If we want to find relief and be healed, we have to find a way to move past our fears and our pride and open up our mouths to share our specific needs with others and with Jesus.

There is a story of a blind man who does this very well:

> *As Jesus approached Jericho, a blind man was sitting by the roadside begging. When he heard the crowd going by, he asked what was happening. They told him, "Jesus of Nazareth is passing by." He called out, "Jesus, Son of David, have mercy on me!" Those who led the way rebuked him and told him to be quiet, but he shouted all the more, "Son of David, have mercy on me!" Jesus stopped and ordered the man to be brought to him. When he came near, Jesus asked him, "What do you want me to do for you?"*
>
> *"Lord, I want to see," he replied. Jesus said to him, "Receive your sight; your faith has healed you." Immediately he received his sight and followed Jesus, praising God. When all the people saw it, they also praised God.*
>
> *- Luke 18:35-43*

He is annoying. He is loud and dramatic and distracting. So they tell him to be quiet...but he shouts all the more. He knows that the only one who can help him is standing right in front of him and he is not going to let anything, pride, fear, or societal norms, stop him from getting the help he needs. So he cries out "Son of David" over and over again, knowing who can save him.

And then Jesus tests his courage even more by asking: "What do you want me to do for you?" It is in this moment, when he has already taken a huge risk and when he feels like his needs should be obvious, that he is invited to get even more specific. Jesus invites him to not only say he needs help, but to share specifically what it is that he needs. And it is when he accepts the invitation and courageously articulates what he wants that he experiences a miracle.

It is not enough to dramatically express our needs (though lament is crucial too; see Chapter 4), but we need to learn how to get specific in who it is we are asking and what it is we are asking for. This will be what leads us to live thriving lives in the midst of chronic pain.

How do we go about doing this? Learning to ask for help requires building a team that we trust. Like any good team leader knows, you rarely are just handed an amazing team. You have to go about building it. Here are four principles of building an effective support team:

CHOOSE YOUR TEAM

As you begin to choose who you want on your team,

look where you are least expecting. Jesus built his team out of thieves, outcasts, and dirty fishermen. These may not be the descriptors you would choose for your friends, but sometimes all it takes is looking at who is already around you in order to find the right people.

Some of the people on my team include a Turkish friend who I met randomly one day at a coffee shop, a neighbor who is a mom of young kids and has availability during the day, a friend who lives overseas who I can call in the middle of the night, a woman who is homeless who understands suffering, and a group of my mom's retired friends in their sixties who are faithful in prayer. They do not all share my same culture, age, or socioeconomic background and yet they have been some of my best supporters.

Of course you can find great friends through your closest circles: in your church, family, or school, but do not limit yourself to only the obvious. Jesus can bring you a team from anywhere.

You need people on your team who are currently suffering, and you also need people on your team who are in relatively stable seasons of their lives. Both can offer you support in their own ways. Build a diverse team from all walks of life and you will have a greater treasure cove of wisdom to lean upon.

As you gather your team, choose who will be in your wider and closer circles. Jesus had different circles of friends. He had his inner circle of three: Peter, James and John. He had the twelve. He had the 72 and he had the crowds. He was vulnerable with everyone, but he had his most vulnerable moments of grief with the three.

Not everyone gets to be in your closest circle. Choose the one to three friends you trust the most to lead you to Jesus. Share the most vulnerably with them. They get to hear the things you will never post on social media. If you have a lot of friends you may need to narrow your list of who it is you share everything with. If you only have a couple friends you may need to find a wider group of people to help carry the load too. Make a conscious choice about who is in what circle, and share appropriately.

One of the most important parts of choosing a team is making an actual invitation. Do not assume that someone is willing to be a part of your inner or wider circle. Ask them. If you are both on the same page about how much they are invested in your life, you will have more freedom to ask for help and they will be more willing to offer it.

KNOW YOUR TEAM

The best teams are ones where everyone operates out of their strengths. Some people are great at cooking meals. Others have more availability and can listen for hours. Some are great at giving practical suggestions. Others will help you laugh. When you know the strengths of the people on your team, you can know who to go to when you have a specific need and you will be more likely to extend grace where there is weakness. One person will never be able to fill all of your needs, but with a team you have access to many different forms of help. Notice what your friends are good at and chances are they will be a lot happier to help when they are able to use their gifts.

It is also important to learn your team's communication preferences. While the best form of communication is always in person, we do operate in a technological world and it is important to know how to use it well. Find out how your friends like to be kept in the loop about how you are doing. Do they appreciate a quick text? A phone call? An email? A social media post? Everyone is a little different and you can help them help you by using the mode of communication that serves them the best.

Learn how your friends best process new information about your situation. Some people see your long emotional word vomit and unfiltered expression as a sign of trust and encourage more of it. Others are served by hearing facts and raw data points to get a better sense of your reality and how they can help. You do not have to change who you are because of someone's personality type, but you can be thoughtful about sharing your life in a way that serves them as they are trying to serve you.

This is the kind of communication that keeps a team

strong for the long term.

LEAD YOUR TEAM

You are the leader of your team. Nobody else can do that for you. You are the one who gets to help your friends know how to help you, such that when they ask you, "What is it that you want me to do for you?" you have an answer.

This requires a significant level of self-leadership and reflection. In order to ask people to help you, you must be self-aware enough to know your real needs. Bill Hybels writes about the importance of self-leadership. He draws insight from the story of King David in 1 Samuel 30. David returns from battle to discover the enemy army has destroyed his campsite. Hybels writes, "In this critical moment David realizes a fundamental truth: he needs to lead himself before he can lead anybody else. Unless he is squared away internally he has nothing much to offer his team. So he found a place of solitude, and there 'David strengthened himself in the Lord his God' (1 Samuel 30:6)."[4] We too have a team to lead through our crisis, and our leadership of our team is only as effective as our leadership of ourselves.

This does not mean that we are the ones who cure ourselves or that it is up to us to have all the answers. But if we are dependent on others to be God for us or to solve all our problems, then we will quickly get defeated. The more we take time to lead ourselves into self awareness and relationship with God, the more we will be able to be honest with our friends about our real needs.

Once we are aware of our needs and have talked to God about them, then we have to actually tell our friends how they can help us. It is foolish to live in a dream world that believes people will just read our minds. They won't. I create Google documents for people on my care team, listing step by step the ways I need help when I have panic attacks or flares of pain. That kind of structure may repulse you, but find what works for you. However you are best at communicating, find a way to tell your friends what you need. They want to help, but everyone, including spouses and closest family members, will not know how to help you unless you have the courage to tell them.

CELEBRATE WITH YOUR TEAM

The friends of the paralyzed man in Mark 2 took the risk to lower him through a roof to meet Jesus, and in return, they got to share in the biggest celebration of their lives. You may not feel like you have any energy to give back to your friends that have chosen to come alongside you, but one of the greatest gifts you can give them is the gift of gratitude and celebration.

Take the time to thank your friends for their help. Affirm them for the risks they are taking to be on the journey with you. Chances are, they have no idea if they are being a real help to you or not, so encourage them along the way.

As you continually ask for help, don't forget to share the victories. Your friends will get defeated alongside you if they only hear about the losses. Tell them your wins too. Even if it is as small as the fact that you got out of bed this morning, it can be a win.

The best teams are ones that receive affirmation and are able to recognize when they have made progress. So do not keep those victories to yourself. Share them every single time and choose into celebration.

Building a team is an art. It requires being vulnerable and opening yourself up to potential rejection. And like every form of art, it takes practice to get really good at it. But the beauty that unfolds as you take the risk to go for it, is more than worth it. Jesus wants to give you an amazing team of people to care for you, but that first requires you to take the risk to learn how to start asking for help.

QUESTIONS FOR REFLECTION

- *What barriers do you face when it comes to asking for help?*
- *What is your current support team like? Who is on it? Where does it need to be strengthened?*
- *What could it look like for you to take a more active role in choosing and building your team?*

The Lame Man's Mat

With perfect calculation
My masterful compilation
Of religious regulation
Confirms my speculation:
His grievance is irrefutable.

At least four pounds
With dirt all around—
How indelicate it sounds
To pick it up off the ground!
It just would be unsuitable.

Just look at the way
He makes this display—
He can't walk away
On the holiest day!
It simply is incomputable.

- Kelly Aalseth, 2018

Chapter 2

DIMINISHED CAPACITY

There is more to do than energy to do it. While this is a common sentiment in normal life, chronic pain accentuates the feeling even more. The need for life management increases while fatigue diminishes our capacity further.

When pain first began for me, I felt like a kid who needed to learn to crawl all over again. Because of the new pain in my lower back, I did not know how to sit without pain so it took a few months of physical therapy and learning to sit with a cushion before I could do computer work again. I had to quit running half marathons because the exercise was too aggressive so I took a year to teach myself how to swim. I had to completely change my diet, and let's face it, as a twenty-five-year-old, I was not a great chef to begin with. And if managing my physical world was not enough, I also had to up my game in seeking counselors and managing my own internal world to be able to emotionally process the reality that I had just been diagnosed with a chronic disorder that would potentially affect me the rest of my life. And I had to learn all of this while my body threw tantrums every time I asked it to do anything.

When our needs begin to outweigh our capacity, our biggest villain is our own inner critic. We fear we are not living up to the standards of our family, friends, doctors, and co-workers, and we feel incapable of doing the things we used to be able to do. Our bodies scream at us when we push too hard and they scream when we do not do enough, drowning out everything except the loud voice of criticism.

When the man at the pool of Bethesda responds to Jesus' invitation to get up and walk, instead of being thrown a party to celebrate this amazing miracle, he is immediately faced with critique. The religious leaders are not impressed by the fact he just did something that was impossible to do. They do not acknowledge his thirty-eight years of paralysis or the fact that his whole life is about to change. They do not offer to help him learn to cook his meals or take him to physical therapy or reintegrate into society. Instead they get hung up on one ridiculous technicality in their laws: "It is the Sabbath; the law forbids you to carry your mat" (John 5:10).

This man was just healed of thirty-eight years of paralysis, and they are concerned that he is caring his mat?! Can you imagine how crushed he would be when he finally learned to trust someone and this is the response he receives? He just did the most courageous thing in his life to vulnerably put his trust in Jesus and to let go of his cynicism, and the first thing anyone says to him is that he is doing something wrong.

We do this to ourselves all the time. Instead of celebrating the risks we are taking in order to manage new pain, we judge ourselves for not being able to do what we think we ought to do. Instead of thanking Jesus for the moments when he gives us strength in our day, we focus on all the ways we feel weak. Instead of recognizing that we are learning to crawl again, we wonder why we are not running marathons. We compare to the standards of our peers and to the standards of our past and convince ourselves that we will never get it right.

Why do we do this? Why did the pharisees witness a miracle and immediately look to their laws? They were terrified of the unknown. They had no explanation for why this man was walking when he had always been that paralyzed beggar at the pool, and so they turned to what they thought could give them a sense of safety. They tried to protect themselves from their loss of control in the only way they knew how: by hiding behind their rules.

Our problem is not that we cannot do what we need to do to survive. God will surely give us the strength to do what he asks of us. Our problem is that we put too much hope in our own standards. When following all the rules that we have created for ourselves is no longer possible, we turn instead to the safety of our own criticism. We try to protect ourselves from the unknown by surrounding ourselves with the familiar tone of our internal judgement.

If we want to be freed from the criticism that haunts us when our capacity diminishes, then we must find a better place of safety. We need to find protection not in our striving to do more or our shame when we do less, but in the grace of Jesus.

Here are three ways to practice letting Jesus' grace supercede the voices of criticism in our lives:

LISTEN FOR THE GRACIOUS TONE OF JESUS

My husband and I slept at my mom's house on New Years Eve so we could get up early for the Rose Parade the next day. Unbeknownst to us, one of the legs of the bed had fallen out, causing the bed to be slightly slanted. I lay awake the whole night, tossing and turning with back pain. The next morning, when I was dragging my feet to get ready, my mom, who had no idea that I had not slept all night, told us to hurry because our friends were waiting for us. I belted out to my mom, "I can't handle this! You don't get what it's like to be me! You care more about your friends than me!" I slammed the door and ran away crying. I was a thirteen-year-old all over again. And to make matters worse, my husband of a few months was there to witness the whole thing.

Suddenly shame welled up inside of me and the voices of critique grew louder and louder: *You're thirty-two years old and you act like this? You know your mom cares about you. She didn't deserve that accusation. Your husband is going to regret marrying you. You're a terrible daughter. You've ruined*

New Years. Pull yourself together!

And as I lay face down, hiding in my snotty pillow from all my crying, my thoughts turned to a memory of just a few weeks earlier, when my four-year-old niece, Araceli, had her own tantrum. It was way past her bedtime and after a day of too much fun, she was not listening to her mom very well. After a gentle scolding from her Papi, she ran back to her mom and gave the most sincere apology, "Mom, I'm SO sorry!" To which my sister quickly replied, "It's ok princess. I forgive you. I know you are so tired."

Just as I was remembering that moment with my sister and Araceli, I felt my husband's arms around me and heard his gentle voice tell me the same thing, "Kelly, you're so tired. It's ok. You're so tired." I was able to take a nap and apologize to my mom and we managed to have a great New Years.

This is the tone that Jesus has for us. It is not the voice of critique and shame, but the voice that acknowledges our tiredness and tells us we have been forgiven. When you are in chronic pain, you are learning to walk in ways you have never known before. You are adjusting to things you did not have to deal with before and are learning a new way of life. In many ways you are like Araceli, growing faster than you can even keep up with, and a tantrum is bound to happen every once in a while. And in those moments, we have to remember that Jesus' tone towards us is always far more gentle than our tone towards ourselves.

Listen for Jesus' tone. When you hear a parent talking lovingly to their child, or a coach encouraging their team, or someone romancing their lover, take note of it. Remember what the voice of grace sounds like and know that Jesus' tone is even more gracious and loving towards you.

NEGATE THE LIE THAT INTENSITY EQUATES TO STRENGTH

Everything in our culture says that intensity is the mark of an admirable person. It is the driven entrepreneurs, the busiest mothers, the sleepless students, the buff athletes that get our respect. We want to be strong and we think that means we must operate at our highest capacity at every minute of every day.

But you cannot get stronger if you are not disciplined enough to be gentle.

I spent several years going to aquatic physical therapy to help with pain management. It is always humbling being in the pool with people forty years older than you. When you are slowly moving your leg back and forth while you hold onto a rail, or doing slow bicycle reps while being held up by a floaty, you certainly do not feel like Michael Phelps. But that gentle motion is crucial to becoming strong.

The same principle is true with music. I remember I could never grow as a musician because every time the music said, "diminuendo," I still looked like I was trying to swing a baseball bat. Sometimes it takes more strength to hold back than it does to be aggressive.

Great leaders also know that operating in one hundred percent capacity all the time is not actually helpful. A good manager leads her team to use seventy percent of their capacity on a daily basis, so when the crises come, they can give their all.

If learning to hold back and be gentle is necessary for becoming a great athlete, musician and leader, then how much more so is it true when we are in chronic pain? If you are in a season where your capacity is diminishing, do not force yourself to strive harder. See it as a gift to learn the art of holding back and let it become a training grounds for growth. You will not be strong in anything unless you first learn to be gentle.

CHANGE YOUR INTERNAL QUESTIONS

If Jesus' tone to us is a tone of grace, and our strength is not only rooted in the amount we produce, then our internal evaluation needs to change too. So often, especially in Western culture, our internal questions are ones like:

- Did I get everything done today?
- Did I do everything right?
- Did I produce enough?

- Did I win?
- Was I successful?
- Did I please others?
- Did I get my ducks in a row for the future?

But, especially if you are in a season of operating with less capacity than you used to have, then these questions need to change. What if, instead, you asked yourself these types of questions at the end of your day:

- Where did I find opportunity for more grace, support, or affection?
- Where did I see beauty today?
- What did I get to enjoy today?
- Did I play well today?
- How did I notice Jesus with me through the day?
- How did I choose to hear Jesus' tone towards me rather than my own critical voice?

If we really believe that Jesus has grace for us, that we cannot heal ourselves, and that we are dependent on his power in our lives to help us get up and walk each day, then we need to be kinder to ourselves in our own internal evaluations such that our questions more closely reflect Jesus' intentions for us.

Perhaps the real victory in your life today is not that you

got everything done, but that you became even more aware of your need for Jesus and your longing for him grew all the more.

QUESTIONS FOR REFLECTION:

- *In what areas of your life do you feel like there is more to do than time to do it? How has your need for life management increased as you have been dealing with chronic pain?*
- *Imagine Jesus talking to you like a loving mother. What does the tone of grace sound like? How do your own thoughts towards yourself match or differ from this tone as you try to manage chronic pain?*
- *List out some better internal questions you can start asking yourself as you evaluate your days. Pick one or two to ask yourself every day this week.*

Before the throne of God above

Before the throne of God above
I have a strong, a perfect plea
A great high priest whose name is Love
Who ever lives and pleads for me
My name is graven on His hands
My name is written on His heart
I know that while in heaven He stands
No tongue can bid me thence depart

When Satan tempts me to despair
And tells me of the guilt within
Upward I look and see Him there
Who made an end to all my sin
Because the sinless Savior died
My sinful soul is counted free
For God the just is satisfied
To look on Him and pardon me

Behold Him there the risen Lamb
My perfect spotless righteousness
The great unchangeable I am
The King of glory and of grace
One with Himself I cannot die
My soul is purchased by His blood
My life is hid with Christ on high
With Christ my Savior and my God!

- Charitie Lees Bancroft, 1841-1892

Chapter 3

UNFLINCHING CONFIDENCE

One of my favorite basketball moments was when Kobe Bryant did not flinch when Matt Barnes pretended to shove a ball in his face. On March 7, 2010, during the third quarter, Barnes tried to intimidate Kobe by moving the ball an inch away from Kobe's face and then quickly pulling it back again. If you watch the clip of the game you will see that Kobe does not even blink.[5] He is so focused on the game that the threat of danger does not scare him in the least.

Having this kind of confidence is critical to thriving through chronic pain. It is what keeps us in the game and prevents us from giving into defeat. But confidence can also be one of the first things to go when new challenges get thrown our way.

Chronic pain can feel like someone is threatening to throw a ball at your face over and over again. When you cannot always predict what your body will do next, or how your friends will react, or how your work or family life will have to change due to fluctuations in pain, it can feel like you are under constant threat of attack. And it is completely understandable to want to respond with fear or panic.

But how do we become people like Kobe who do not even flinch when something unexpected comes our way?

How do we grow in confidence to be able to get up and walk with Jesus and not let the fear of new challenges paralyze us, especially when we have a history of pain to legitimize those fears?

There were two days in my past seven years of pain that my confidence felt the most threatened. The first was the day right before my wedding day. It was not that I lacked confidence in who I was about to marry—I was completely convinced that he was the right partner for me—but it was a confidence that I would even make it down the aisle.

My wedding day was the most anticipated day of my life. Not only had I dreamt about it since I was a kid, and thought about all the little details every time I attended someone else's wedding (long before I even met my husband), but there was so much dreaming and planning for months leading up to it. Even though event planning is a big part of my job on InterVarsity staff, this was definitely the biggest and most emotionally-consuming event of my life.

The week before the big day, with 300 of our family and friends all ready to come to town to celebrate with us, I had the worst flare of pain to date. I developed burning mouth syndrome where every nerve in my mouth was activated. I felt like I had a second degree sunburn in my mouth. As my fiancé went to go pick up the tuxes and my roommate was baking my wedding cake, I checked myself into the doctor to begin IV treatment therapy, hoping that something—anything—could calm the pain.

While I sat there with needles in my arms and more pain than I once thought imaginable, I wondered if the day I had been anticipating and planning for so long, was going to happen at all. And as if my confidence was not dwindling enough, the doctor came to me and said, "Is there any way to postpone the wedding?" How was I possibly supposed to be unflinching in that moment?

Another test of my confidence came the day I went in for my first surgery that was necessary for my protection from uterine cancer. I had spent several months gearing myself up for it mentally and anticipating how my nerves might respond to the trauma. I worried about the thought of cancer and was ready to have it over with.

But moments before they were supposed to operate, it was like another basketball came straight to my face. The anesthesiologists could not find my veins. They tried over three dozen times. Every nurse and doctor in the entire clinic surrounded my bed as I screamed and began to hyperventilate from the pain of the needles. Finally, the surgeon came in and said, "We will just have to cancel." What? I was more than devastated.

When I think about moments like these when confidence is ready to crumble, I think about two of my heroes in the Bible who were even more unflinching than Kobe: Mary the mother of Jesus, and the woman from Syrophoenicia.

In John 2:1-11, Mary is also at a wedding and is faced with the threat of the party having to end poorly. The host of the party runs out of wine and in Middle-Eastern culture that was pretty much the most shameful thing imaginable. Rather than letting her friends be shamed by their whole community, Mary looks to her son, Jesus, and tells him to do something about it. But instead of quickly running off to the local convenience store to purchase more wine, Jesus does the unexpected and tells her it is not his time to do a miracle.

Mary could have seen that as a slammed door, a ball in her face. What did he mean it wasn't his time? Worse than shaming your friends is shaming your own mother. But somehow Mary is not fazed at all. She does not let the unexpected answer prevent her from having confidence that there is still a way to do the impossible. Instead of crumbling in defeat, Mary confidently tells the servants, "Do whatever he tells you" (John 2:5). Essentially, she is saying, "I don't care if it is not your time Jesus, do it anyway." She is not about to put an end to the party. Her confidence is unflinching.

The woman from Syrophoenicia also does not flinch when Jesus gives her an answer she does not expect. (Mark 7:24-30) She hears that Jesus is a healer and so she comes to him, begging him to heal her daughter of a demon. But instead of just offering her the healing she asked for, Jesus decides to engage her in conversation about the racism she'd experienced her whole life, pointing out the obvious that she is a Greek and it is the Jews who were the favored people of God. Why should she expect healing from Jesus?

Imagine her devastation. She came all this way, hoping for rescue for her daughter, risking her reputation by asking for something from a leader of an ethnicity that she was not supposed to affiliate with, and then her worst fears are realized. She is an unwelcome Greek woman and Jesus not only does not give her what she wants, but he directly acknowledges her lack of privilege. But somehow she still does not take no for an answer. She boldly asks Jesus for even just "the crumbs" of his healing.

The confidence of each of these women lead Jesus to change his answer to their requests from "not yet" to "ok, right now," and they both go down in history as people who saw incredible miracles because of their faith. Jesus not only does not let the wedding party stop, but he turns 180 gallons of water into the best wine they had ever tasted. And in the same minute that the Syrophoenician woman cleverly sticks her foot into Jesus' seemingly slammed door, her daughter is delivered of her demon.

When we have this kind of unflinching confidence, we get to see Jesus do the impossible. What we once saw as the biggest barrier, we see Jesus break through as if it was nothing. But how do we gain this kind of confidence? How do we possibly have this kind of faith when we cannot see the end of the story? When it feels like that ball is about to hit us straight in the face and there is no way around it? How do we grow in our confidence that Jesus has our back and will lead us to victory?

RECOGNIZE JESUS IS DOING THE FIGHTING

In the book of Genesis, Jacob blesses his son Joseph with this powerful image of an archer who is propped up on the hands of God as he fights:

> *"The archers will attack him, they will shoot at him and oppose him. But his bow will remain steady, and his hands will be skillful; because of the hands of the Mighty One of Jacob"*
>
> *- Genesis 49:23-24, NET*

When you are in chronic pain, it can feel like you are fighting on your own, and that if you let our guard down for even just a second, that you will be defeated. The attack is a guarantee. You may not know if it will come today or tomorrow, but you know the pain will rear its ugly head soon enough. And this can make you feel like you have to be on the defensive 24/7, ready to face whatever comes your way.

But preparation alone will not make you grow in unflinching confidence. Joseph was able to fight "because of the hands of the Mighty One." Joseph may have the bow and arrow in his hands. He may look like the one fighting the battle. But the only way he has strength to leave his arms up so long is because the powerful hand of God is propping him up and guiding his bow. In reality, God is the one doing the bulk of the heavy lifting.

Jesus is not passively sitting by cheering us on. He is actively engaged in our fight. The Bible describes Jesus at the right hand of God interceding on our behalf. (Romans 8:34) He is literally standing in between us and that which will lead to our destruction. Our confidence grows when we remember that Jesus is the one doing the pleading on our behalf. He is doing the work that we will never be able to accomplish on our own.

We may know this reality in our heads, but letting it translate to our hearts when pain is always in front of us is difficult. Sometimes we need something to hang onto that goes beyond just words on a page. It may help to visualize or draw the image in Genesis 49 or to sing the hymn at the beginning of this chapter in order to meditate even more on the reality of God's role in your life as you face the constant threat of pain.

CHOOSE TO BE HELD

Letting Jesus fight on our behalf requires us to choose to be held. The arms of the archer cannot be held up by the strength of God if there is resistance to his embrace. This may very well be the hardest part of growing confidence. We want to be superheroes. We want to be like Kobe and look like we are the best at our game. But, counterintuitively, the thing that will grow our confidence the most is our ability to be vulnerable.

When I finished the IV treatment the day before my wedding, my mouth still burning with pain, and my fears increasingly growing, I came home to a living room full of extended family. They had flown in from all around the country and were excited and ready to celebrate. Normally, this would be one of my dreams come true, to have everyone I loved in the same room ready for the biggest party of my life. But, in that moment, it was my worst nightmare.

I knew I had a choice to make. I could choose to put on a false confidence that everything was just fine, muster up a few smiles and make up an excuse to get out of there, or I could choose to be honest. Here was my whole family wanting to love me, and the thing I needed the most was to be able to fall apart.

I made my decision and ran into my mom's arms and

wept. I wept with my whole family staring at me awkwardly, unsure of what to do. I looked into my mom's eyes and voiced my deepest fear, "Mom, am I going to make it down the aisle?" "Of course, honey. We are all going to get you down that aisle."

Choosing to be held is one of the most courageous things we can do. It is only when we fall into the arms of Jesus and let him embrace us like a mother, that our confidence can grow to the point that we are unflinching. His arms are always open towards us, but we get to decide if we will let down our pride enough to receive his embrace.

It is not enough to pray or to ask our friends for help. We must also learn to receive love from God and our community. The next time you hear God whisper his love to you or hear a friend offer you their help, take a moment and breathe and intentionally let down your guard so you can actually enjoy the gift that has been given to you.

APPEAL TO JESUS' CHARACTER

The Syrophoenician woman and Mary did not take no for an answer from Jesus, because they believed his reaction to their circumstance did not line up with what they knew to be true about his character. Mary believed that her son cared about protecting the honor of their friends and that he cared deeply about her. The Syrophoenician woman believed Jesus was bigger than societal norms and had enough healing for everyone. So they were confident to keep asking because they were confident in the kindness and integrity of who they were asking.

When the surgeon told me that she could not go through with the surgery after so many attempts at finding my vein, I remembered the Syrophoenician woman and appealed to Jesus' character. Jesus, you are better than this. You wouldn't alert me to something pre-cancerous, torture me through months of anticipation and an hour of needle prodding only to have me walk away with nothing to show for it. You are kinder than that, Jesus. I stopped everyone in the room and said firmly, "Wait. Try for ten more minutes and then decide. I will calm down." I started praying Psalm 23 aloud over and over again, believing that Jesus was the Good Shepherd and would carry me ahead to green pastures.

The doctors exclaimed, "I don't know what you're doing, but it's working. Keep doing it." Eventually they did get the vein and I went through with a successful surgery. My husband told me afterwards that it was other-worldly how much I calmed down when I was reciting the scripture.

Jesus is not a vending machine that gives us everything we want whenever we want it. We see from the stories of Mary and the Syrophoenician woman that there are times he does say "no" or "not yet." But when we know him well enough and we start to recognize consistency in his tone and character, we can ask him confidently for what we want because we know he is good.

Comedian Jimmy Kimmel made a hilarious video of parents pranking their kids at Christmas time.[6] They gave their kids a terrible Christmas gift (like a rotten banana or a half-eaten sandwich) and recorded their reactions. The younger kids had full on melt downs, but the older kids quickly recognized the joke and pleaded with their parents to give them the real gift. They knew that the gift was inconsistent with the love of their parent and freely expressed their dissatisfaction.

Children are confident to boldly ask for what they want when they know and trust their parent. The more we meditate on the reality that God is fighting on our behalf and the more we allow ourselves to be held by him, the more we will know him, and the more we know him, the more we will be confident to ask him for what we need.

QUESTIONS FOR REFLECTION:

- *In what areas of your life are you needing confidence? Where are you tempted to panic or be afraid?*
- *Imagine Jesus lifting up your arms as you hold a bow and arrow towards those things that you fear, as you fight through chronic pain. What does it feel like as you put all your weight on his arms? Is there anything he wants to say to you as you do?*
- *List out adjectives you know to be true of God's character. Ask God to take care of the things you fear and to grow your confidence that he will answer you because of his loving character.*

Release without Revelation

It hurts…but
Been 7 years…but
Six months…but
No one knows…but
Just gets worse…but
Can't sleep…but
Can't eat…but
Too much…but
Make it stop…but
Stop…but
STOP
(breathe)
No "but." Know what?
Your "but God"
eclipses and
dismisses —
please no more quick fixes-
what I've been trying to say:
I am in PAIN.
Long standing, never ending
pain pain pain pain PAIN.

I am in pain. He is "I am."
Both are true
but you…you
think your "but God"
can pass
as an answer to
the vast
complexity and mystery
that no man in
life's history
has ever comprehended:
the answer to
Pain.

If you must
use your "but"
at least let me breathe….
long enough to consider,
if he is so much bigger
then surely he's ok
listening to my heartbeat of
"It hurts" and "I don't know"
Letting the echo linger
until silence
becomes my refuge.

- Kelly Aalseth, 2017

Chapter 4

THE POWER OF RELEASE

Three times in one year, one of my tires blew out while I was driving. Thankfully I was safe every time but I was beginning to get annoyed by how expensive and interruptive it was to have to keep going back to the tire shop. I soon realized my problem: I was putting too much air in my tires. I kept going to the gas station to pump my tires full of air, when what I really needed was to learn to release some of the air out.

Knowing when and how to release is crucial to thriving with chronic pain. We are constantly being filled with new emotions, lessons, hopes and disappointments because of the pain and if we never stop to let any of that out, then we will explode like my tires.

Jesus knows we cannot keep stuffing things down without letting them out. He knows the power of release. In Mark 5:25-34, there is woman with a chronic disorder that caused her to bleed for twelve years. No amount of money or doctors was able to heal her. Not only did this cause physical trauma but it meant she was "unclean" and outcast from society and unable to publically worship. She heard Jesus was in town and believed if she could just sneak in and quickly touch him without anyone looking, she would be healed. Sure enough her touch of Jesus healed her of her bleeding.

But Jesus knew she needed more than that. He knew she needed to release. So he called her out in front of the entire crowd (her worst nightmare) and invited her to share her story. The text says she told Jesus "the whole truth" (Mark 5:33). We can imagine what that sounded like: *I tried this doctor but they didn't take my insurance. This other doctor didn't believe me. My husband stopped listening because I was too "emotional." How was I supposed to take care of my family with all this fatigue? I tried this medicine but I couldn't tolerate the side effects. The people at church tell me it's my fault. I'm trying to understand the medical system but there are too many papers that I can't read...* And on and on she went. With everyone listening.

Jesus knows the healing power of release. He knows we cannot just stuff the pain. We have to let it out.

I was at Catalina Island for an InterVarsity conference, doing prayer ministry for students, when suddenly the pain in my mouth began to escalate rapidly. I contemplated if I should leave quietly and try to go to bed or get on a boat and go to the nearest hospital. But before I could form my plan, a student came up to me and said, "I want to pray for you." She prayed simply, "Jesus take away Kelly's pain and give her a great doctor," and turned around to sit down. I thanked Jesus for showing me he sees me and continued to plan my escape from the camp.

But then, all of a sudden, something happened that I had never experienced before. My jaw started moving on its own accord. It started opening and closing and clicking. A few other friends came around me and asked me if I were to assign a number to the pain, what would it be. I said a "ten." I began to feel the freedom to weep and cry out to God, telling him (and all the students around me) how badly it hurt. Soon, my neck and back began to click and move too, without me consciously doing so. It was as if God himself was giving me a chiropractic adjustment. My friends asked me again what number I would assign the pain. I said, "It's a two." We all sat in disbelief and praised God for bringing such fast and miraculous relief.

After that prayer session, the pain continued to rise and fall for about five months, but through continued prayer, a great physical therapist and dentist (also an answer to that student's prayers), I can now say that I have my mouth back. Jesus used a lot of people to heal my mouth, but he began with a powerful moment of release. He began my healing by showing me it was okay to weep in front of the very students that I was supposed to be ministering to. He was inviting me to literally release the tension that had been compounding in my spine from constant pain.

We were created to be able to release pain. When a child scrapes a knee or gets teased by someone on the playground, it is healthy for them to be able to cry or express that emotion to someone. But as adults, our egos take over and we become afraid to be messy in front of others. Moreover, we are afraid to be honest in front of God. We are afraid of coming to the end of ourselves.

I recently went through about three months of depression due to pain and to some side effects from medications, and what was harder than depression itself was being honest about the ways I was depressed. It terrified me to acknowledge my dark feelings and I was scared of becoming suicidal. But Jesus invited me, in the same way that he invited the bleeding woman, to be honest with him and with my community. I told my husband about the depression and his response to me was, "It's ok if the dark thoughts are too overwhelming. It's ok to get some help." He helped me make a plan to communicate with my doctors about the medication and continued to treat me with love and dignity.

Jesus showed me, through the compassion of my husband, that he is not scared of depression. Psalm 139:12 says, "Even the darkness will not be dark to you; the night will shine like the day, for darkness is as light to you." Not even darkness is dark to God. He can handle all of our thoughts and emotions.

John Ortberg, in a sermon to InterVarsity staff, said, "On the cross, (Jesus) did not say, 'The Lord is my shepherd, I shall not want'. On the cross he did not say 'The Lord is my light and my salvation'. On the cross he said, 'My God, my

God, why have you forsaken me?"[7] If God can handle this kind of raw despair from his own son, then surely he can take it from us.

I woke up in the middle of the night one night with depression and pain, and I practiced being honest. Instead of trying to console myself with God is good and he is my shepherd, I blurted out, "God, I can't find you right now! Where are you? I have to see you. Help!" I worried if my husband would think I had lost my faith, but I never felt closer to God than in that moment. I knew God not only could handle my release of desperation, but that he was inviting it.

Jesus loves it when we are brutally honest with him. He wants to hear all of it. He wants us to release the pain and not stuff it down. He wants us to tell him how we hurt, how we are tired, and what we are fearing. He wants to hear our story. He knows we need to let it out, and he tells us that we are safe with him as we do.

How do you start to release your pain to Jesus? Here are a few tools to help you get started:

WRITE YOUR OWN LAMENT

Start by reading some examples. Psalms and the book of Lamentations can be a great place to start:

I have been deprived of peace;

I have forgotten what prosperity is.
Then I thought, "My future is lost,
as well as my hope from the Lord."
Remember my affliction and my homelessness,
the wormwood and the poison.
I continually remember them
and have become depressed.

- Lamentations 3:17-20, CSB

Let yourself feel the emotion of the writer and underline the places where you feel a connection.

Imagine Jesus is right there with you and begin to list out the things that you are grieving. What is hurting in your body right now? What relational interactions have been difficult recently? What losses are you grieving? Are you unable to do something you used to be able to do? Is there a dream that you fear is now dead?

Resist the urge to filter or qualify. Tell Jesus everything that hurts, even the seemingly small things.

USE ART TO HELP YOU EXPRESS YOUR EMOTIONS

Take a risk and turn the list you have written into something more creative. Write a poem using some of the themes you have written down. Paint a picture that captures your feelings. Design a garden or make a craft that symbolizes some of the things you've lost. Write a song or do a dance that captures the grief.

You can use an art form that is familiar to you or try something different. Sometimes using a new form of art can help us unlock inner emotions that we had not known were there. Do not worry about impressing anyone or publishing your work. This is just between you and God so, as much as you can, let go of pressure to do it well.

You can also use the art of others to help you lament. At the beginning of each chapter of this book is a poem or song. Pick one that grabs your attention and reflect on it for a while. Ask yourself how you relate and tell God your thoughts and feelings.

Turn on some music and sing along or let yourself cry as you listen. Or look at a painting and let it help you tune into the things you have been holding inside.

There is no right way to lament. The important thing is to ask Jesus to help you release and to be honest with him.

RELEASE THE LIES YOU ARE BELIEVING SURROUNDING THE PAIN, AND AFFIRM WHAT IS TRUE

Release does not always take the form of lament or emotional expression. Sometimes we need to release the thoughts in our minds that are not from Jesus. We constantly write narratives in our minds about what is happening to us. Jesus invites us to let go of all the narratives we have written for ourselves that are not actually true and to affirm the truth of his love, grace and power in our lives.

Depending on your personality and upbringing, there are certain false narratives that you write for yourself more regularly than others. The book, "Enneagram Transformations: Releases and Affirmations for healing your personality type" by Don Richard Riso has a great list of lies you might believe based on your personality type.[8]

I took some ideas from that book and then created my own list for myself. I need to release these lies and affirm these truths on a daily basis. The more you grow in your own self awareness the more you will be able to recognize what you may need to release regularly.

Here is my list:

Things to Release:

- my dread of the unknown future
- my feeling of being all alone
- my need to know I am doing the right thing
- my need to be my own doctor
- my need to look like I have it all together
- my paranoia and worst-case scenario thinking
- my jealousy of others who are well
- my inner critic

- my feeling of being incapable of functioning on my own
- my negativity and self-focus

Things to Affirm:

- God is the keeper of my life and is in control of my future.
- God is with me and I am surrounded by a community who have my back.
- Whether I am right or wrong, God is still in control and I live under his grace.
- God is the good doctor and my shepherd, and I can surrender to him and trust his guidance.
- It is ok to ask for help and to feel powerless.
- God wants me to "have life, and have it to the full" (John 10:10).
- Everybody is different and illness will not deter from God's calling on my life.
- God loves me and is proud of me.
- God has given me a brain and strength and community to help me live. He has given me courage.
- Jesus is the resurrected Lord and has the final victory.

I take this list out every morning in my prayer time and say each one of them aloud. If one resonates more than another I will linger there a little longer and ask Jesus if he wants to say anything to me about it. Something powerful happens in my soul as I let go of the lies and hang onto the truth of Jesus.

We are not meant to stuff down all the thoughts and emotions that come to us through chronic pain. Jesus wants us to be honest and knows that release is a crucial part of our healing. Take his invitation and tell him how you are doing. He wants to hear your story.

QUESTIONS FOR REFLECTION:

- *When was the last time you were totally honest with God about how you felt about the pain you face? How do you feel about acknowledging that you are at the end of yourself?*
- *Make your own list of things to release and affirm. Spend some time refining or adding to your list at the end of each day as you notice common themes.*
- *Try making your own lament. Don't worry about making a masterpiece. Just express your pain to God in the most unfiltered and honest way that you can. Imagine him with you as you do and trust that he is keeping you safe as you offer your heart to him.*

Dear Doctor

Dear Doctor,
Why do you hate my other doctors?
It's confusing.

Dear Doctor,
I found you myself. Is that ok?
I'm trying my best.

Dear Doctor,
Will you help me if you don't know what to do?
Nobody does.

Dear Doctor,
Why do you say I'm too young to hurt?
I do.

Dear Doctor,
I'm not trying to trick you or get my way.
Teach me?

Dear Doctor,
I'm not the best at explaining.
Can I try again?

Dear Doctor,
You left so fast…
Did I do something wrong?

Dear Doctor,
I guess you are glad I'm gone now.
I know I'm confusing.

Dear Doctor,
I have nowhere else to go.
Except to that other doctor...that you hate.

Sincerely,
a child of divorced doctors

- Kelly Aalseth, 2018

Chapter 5

OVERWHELMING OPTIONS

When you break a bone or come down with a cold, knowing what to do can be fairly simple. Do what the doctor says and use common sense and you will be just fine. But when dealing with something chronic or an illness that is less understood, knowing how to find relief or healing can be much more difficult.

We live in an age of too many choices. In the same way that it now takes ten minutes to choose between hundreds of brands of pasta sauces in the grocery store, it can also feel overwhelming to know how to navigate the large amount of resources available to us to aid in our healing. And when chronic pain has no obvious remedy, we can easily find ourselves paralyzed under the weight of too many decisions. What kind of doctor do I see? Which one of the fifty popular diets should I follow? Do I trust WebMD or do I do what the grandmother of my neighbor's second cousin is advising me to do?

How do we use healing resources (medications, therapies, nutrients, advice, life rhythms, spiritual disciplines, etc.) wisely without giving up under the exhaustion of decision making?

First, we must remember that all these resources are a gift from God and he designed us to have creative access to them. He loves it when we research and discover new things in his creation that help bring relief from pain.

Genesis 1:27-29 says, "So God created mankind in his own image, in the image of God he created them; male and female he created them. God blessed them and said to them, 'Be fruitful and increase in number; fill the earth and subdue it. Rule over the fish in the sea and the birds in the sky and over every living creature that moves on the ground.' Then God said, "I give you every seed-bearing plant on the face of the whole earth and every tree that has fruit with seed in it. They will be yours for food."

God created the world with order and rhythm and artistic design and then created us to do the same. He made us in his image, giving us access to all of his creation so that we might thrive. God designed us to be researchers and harvesters and co-creators, and to enjoy the process of discovery.

I spent a whole day designing Excel bar graphs and charts in an attempt to see how my pain levels fluctuate with my diet and menstrual cycle. By the end of the day I started judging myself as if my trying to find answers was a sign of my lack of faith, but then God stopped me, saying, "Kelly, I love that you spent a day making Excel charts. I love that you are doing research and gathering data. You are made in my image and I gave you that creativity and intelligence. Have fun with it!"

God loves it when we make medical discoveries and learn new things about how to be healthy. It was in his design that we would learn to create with him. Jesus himself creatively used the things of the earth when he performed miracles. He used mud on a man's eyes to heal him of his blindness. He used a boy's fish and bread to feed five thousand people. He gives us resources so that we can use them.

But where we can go wrong is when we let those resources become like gods: when we see the doctors or the medications or therapies as greater than the God who designed them. I love how the writer of Genesis accounts the creation of the sun and moon. In a time where sun worship was prevalent, he writes: "God made two great lights—the greater light to govern the day and the lesser light to govern the night." The sun and moon are two of the most powerful things that help us to live, and yet they do not even deserve a real name. They are just a "greater and lesser light."

This is the way we must think of the different resources available to us. They are wonderful gifts from God that are ours to enjoy, but they are not worthy of our worship. They are not worthy of occupying our minds so much that we become overcome with fear and anxiety as we try to figure out which ones to use. They do not get the final say on when we are to act and when we are to rest. Jesus is the only one who gets to do that. Jesus is the only one worthy of our worship.

My friends in North India understand this reality well. I had the honor of getting to go to India when I was seventeen and visit a friend's hospital. One day a young girl came in with a snake bite on her hand. The wound was so bad I could not even tell she had a hand anymore. The doctor gave her antivenom serum to remove the poison and dressed the wound to save her hand, using every resource he had available. She was at death's door. The resources were inadequate and it may have been too late. We soon left the hospital to move on to other parts of India and a few days later we got a call from the same doctor. He said, "Praise be to God, the young girl was completely healed!" Whatever happened? We were in disbelief. He said matter of factly, "Jesus healed her." Later, several members of her extended family put their faith in Jesus too.

This doctor used the tools he had, but he did not give them his worship. His ultimate trust was in Jesus to do the healing.

How do we become like my friends in North India and use the gifts Jesus has given us of medication, nutrition, and therapy, doing all that we can to live with wisdom, discipline, and self control, while also remembering that Jesus is the one with the ultimate power and control over our lives?

Here are a few suggestions:

KEEP ADDING TO YOUR "ART KIT"

When dealing with something chronic, we have to retrain ourselves to stop believing there is just one cause and one solution to our problem. Perhaps someone will discover a direct cause and an easy cure to your pain someday, but more likely than not, you will need to find several different coping strategies to keep you going for the long haul. This process can feel much more like an art than a science.

I can drive myself up a wall trying to hope in every little thing that someone suggests to me. *Try this supplement. Stop eating this particular food. Stretch this muscle. Try this mouthwash. Pray in this particular fashion.* And when each of those things don't cure me, I not only feel disappointed but I feel like I somehow am letting down the person who suggested it to me.

I find it helpful, when I am overwhelmed with suggestions for my healing, to think of it less like solving a math equation and more like putting more supplies into my art kit. It is not that adding in all the right strategies will equate to my healing. Rather, I get to choose from many options of tools to make life a little more beautiful on a given day. An artist may choose to use a paintbrush one day and colored pencils the next. In the same way, strengthening exercises may be just what I need one day, and playing games and relaxing may be what helps me the next. It is less about finding the one perfect tool and more about expanding your options to choose from. Of course, if a doctor gives you medication you should be careful to follow their instructions, but sometimes there is more creative room to experiment than we think.

Some of the things in my "art kit" include a cushion to sit on, peppermint gum, a natural mouthwash, a muscle cream, the FODMAP diet, a foam roller, tennis, swimming, the Psalms, Epsom Salt, and poetry books.

I did not know about all of these things immediately. Some of them took months to discover. If you are just beginning to add to your "art kit", remember it will take time. Focus on finding one tool at a time and eventually you will have a beautiful collection of things you can work with. If you have been at it for a while, look back to see all the different creative resources you have discovered over time. See them as gifts from God and thank him for them.

Enjoy the journey of discovery and know that as you are searching you are doing so with your creator. You are not all alone trying to find a needle in a haystack to magically cure you. You are on an adventurous journey with your Father who wants you to thrive.

LISTEN TO JESUS, THE MASTER ARTIST

There may be days that we are facing pain and it is not

obvious which tool will help us in that particular moment. We must remember that Jesus created us and has the most expertise in helping us creatively find relief. We can ask him for wisdom and he will direct us in what to do.

I make it a habit to ask Jesus at least once a week: "What would you have me do for my health this week?" And then I am quiet and listen for an answer.[9] Sometimes different thoughts will pop into my mind: "Drink more water. Watch your sugar intake. Go to the gym." Other times the answers will surprise me: "Don't dwell on it. Rest as much as you can. Watch a movie with your husband." And other times there will be more urgent answers: "Go to the doctor immediately."

On a day where the burning pain in my mouth was very high and we did not know why, my husband and I stopped to pray and ask Jesus what to do in that moment. The thought came into my head that I should go see the dentist the next morning. Sure enough there was a horribly decayed wisdom tooth in my mouth that needed to be removed. Unless we had stopped to pray, I never would have thought to go back to the dentist (because I had been there just a couple of months before).

God created you and he gives you his Holy Spirit to guide you. Jesus says, "But when he, the Spirit of truth, comes, he will guide you into all the truth" (John 16:13). Allow the Spirit to guide you. He knows everything about you. Is he not the best person to ask for wisdom when we do not know what to do?

One of the biggest barriers we can have in learning to hear the voice of Jesus is the pressure we put on ourselves to hear his "one correct answer." God is far more creative than that. If we miss his voice the first time, he will speak to us in another way. He has access to all of creation and is not dependent on us to find the one resource that will magically cure us. He can use whatever he wants, and he can direct us to those resources using many forms of communication. So let go of the pressure of getting it right and let the master artist guide you through the creative process.

EXPECT THE UNEXPECTED

To be a great artist, you must learn to expect the unexpected. In my theater classes, we did not just memorize our lines but we learned strategies for improvisation so the show would still go on when someone forgot their lines. Great basketball players do not just learn the textbook answer of where to place their feet to make a shot. They assume their rhythm will get upset and they have to learn the art of the game when it is impossible to get their feet in the "right position."

It is the same for us in dealing with chronic pain. It is not enough to have a plan for what to do when things are going as expected. We also need to learn to expect the unexpected and ask Jesus for what to do in those times as well.

I have my tools ready: I go to physical therapy, I eat as best as I know how, I have my prayer times, and I know my need for church and community. But I also, not pessimistically but wisely, assume that there will be days or weeks that I won't be able to do any of those things. Perhaps pain will be too high for me to tackle the gym. Maybe panic or depression will come so strongly that I can no longer manage the internal voices in my head on my own. Maybe I will not be able to sit through a church service because my back pain is too much. Maybe I will eat something by accident, not knowing the ingredients, and it will send me home sooner than I wanted.

So I also ask Jesus for some back up plans. I talk with my coworkers about what to do on the days that I have to cancel meetings. My close friends are on speed dial and know how to help me when I have a flare of pain. I know how to carve out some extra space to just meditate on Jesus' grace. I allow myself to wait, sometimes doing nothing at all. (More on this in Chapter 6.)

Great artists are not reliant on their art materials alone. They can work with whatever they have and call it beautiful. We do not need to be discouraged when our rhythms and strategies are thrown off, because Jesus is the master artist and can help us learn new ways of creativity. So we hold our healing tools loosely.

NEGATE THE LIE THAT IT IS YOUR FAULT

When there is no obvious reason for your pain, you can easily be tempted to believe that it is because you just haven't found the right tools yet or are not using them correctly. This is a lie. It is not your fault that you are in chronic pain. It is not God's punishment on your life. There is not something you have done, or not done, that you must now make up for. There is not something you are doing that is causing Jesus to stop loving you.

Romans 8:1-2 says, "there is now no condemnation for those who are in Christ Jesus, because through Christ Jesus the law of the Spirit who gives life has set you free from the law of sin and death."

As God exposes sin in our lives, we must confess it and continue to let him free us of addictions and bad habits and shape us to become more like him. But because of Jesus' death and resurrection we are no longer accused.

As I learn to be disciplined to use my different tools of eating well and exercising and doing what doctors tell me to do, I must also be disciplined in leaning more and more into grace. Jesus does not look down on me saying, "You shouldn't have eaten that extra cookie. Now I will send your nerves into uncontrollable shock." Or "How foolish you were to miss that therapy appointment. Now you are going to really feel the consequences." It is my own inner voice that says those kinds of things. Jesus looks at me with compassion and says, "I see you are trying so hard to do what is right. I am so proud of you. I hate seeing you in so much pain. Hang onto me and we will get through this day."

As we look for different things to bring us relief from pain, we are not being tested to see if we can find the "one right answer." We are being invited to be creative with our creator so that we may have life to the full. As you take the risk to try new things to aid in your healing, do it knowing that God is Lord over all creation and delights in you as you discover it with him.

QUESTIONS FOR REFLECTION:

- *What resources have you already discovered to help you with pain? Spend some time thanking God for the things that have been helpful to you.*
- *In what ways are you tempted to be too reliant on your "art materials" or your search for more healing tools? Ask God for forgiveness and to help you redirect your hope to him.*
- *How are you tempted to believe that chronic pain is your fault? Ask Jesus to tell you what he thinks about you and your situation.*

The Thought of God

To think of Thee is almost prayer,
And is outspoken praise;
And pain can even passive thoughts
To actual worship raise.

O Lord! I live always in pain,
My life's sad undersong,
Pain in itself not hard to bear,
But hard to bear so long.

Little sometimes weighs more than much,
When it has no relief;
A joyless life is worse to bear
Than one of active grief.

And yet, O Lord! A suffering life
One grand ascent may dare;
Penance, not self-imposed, can make
The whole of life a prayer.

All murmurs lie inside Thy Will
Which are to Thee addressed;
To suffer for Thee is our work,
To think of Thee our rest.

Frederick William Faber, 1814-1863

Chapter 6

THE BEST DOCTORS MAKE YOU WAIT

I have a love-hate relationship with waiting rooms. One time I was waiting to get an ultrasound to see if I needed surgery, and "Phantom of the Opera" was playing through the loudspeakers in the clinic. Real cheery choice of music. Let's just say I would choose to curl up with a book on my own couch over trying to make time pass faster in a doctor's office any day. On the other hand, when I have to wait a long time to see a doctor, I know I have a higher chance of getting good care. Recently I waited an hour past my appointment time before getting called in to see the doctor. It was annoying for sure, but as I sat there playing games on my phone, a lady leaned over and told me, "You are going to have a great experience. I have been a client of his for years and he is so kind and a great listener. He is the only one who has been patient enough to get me on the right medication." When I finally did get to see the doctor, he had to excuse himself for a moment to go help an elderly woman who was on the verge of throwing up. This was a good doctor.

Efficiency and great care rarely go hand in hand. Thankfully, God does not have the same problem of not being able to care for more than one person at a time. He does not make us wait because he has "bigger problems" to attend to. But we also cannot assume that every time he does make us wait that it means he is a bad doctor. In fact, it may just very well mean that he is the best doctor.

Our thought process is inconsistent: We say we want someone to listen to our full story and provide a thorough and effective plan for our healing, but not if it takes more than five minutes. How can we truly be known and experience comfort from anyone if we are not willing for them to take any time with us? But our idolatry of quick-fixes and instant gratification makes us feel like if it is not efficient, then it is not compassion.

Naaman, of the Bible, is known as “a great man...highly regarded...a valiant soldier” (2 Kings 5:1), but he too cannot handle waiting. He gets diagnosed with leprosy and goes to Elisha the prophet for healing. When Elisha tells him he needs to take seven dips into the river to get cured, he humorously expresses his dismay:

“I thought that he (Elisha) would surely come out to me and stand and call on the name of the LORD his God, wave his hand over the spot and cure me” (2 Kings 5:11).

How often do we feel that way? *You want me to do what? Seven times? Why can’t you just snap your fingers and fix me already?* We do not like it when God makes us wait. And we do not like it when his choosing to involve us in the healing process requires more time to produce results. Sometimes we would much rather have what we want quickly than actually take the time to engage with our Creator.

But even in our impatience God is sympathetic to our waiting.

Seven dips in a river was too long for Naaman to wait to experience healing. But what about the paralyzed man at the pool of Bethesda? He had to wait thirty-eight years. Thirty-eight! That is six years longer than I have been alive. I cannot imagine that kind of wait. And yet Jesus himself acknowledges that it has been a long time.

Joni Eareckson Tada, a quadripalegic of over 50 years now, says it well: "Jesus is the Ancient of Days who scattered the galaxies across the heavens and laid the very foundation of the earth. What would thirty-eight years be to Him? Less than a heartbeat!...In our Lord's humanity, however, thirty-eight years was more than His whole lifetime. He knows time in a personal, experiential way. As the writer of Hebrews said, 'We don't have a priest who is out of touch with our reality.'"[10]

Jesus does not condemn us for being annoyed or even bitter or angry about waiting. Whether you have been hurting two weeks too long or seventy years too long, it is still too long. And Jesus gets it.

There are some things we will never understand about human suffering, and it is far too simple of a statement to say that the suffering you face today is there solely to help you know God better or to make you a better person. God is not so cruel to look at our torture and smile because of the character boost we receive from it. Jesus himself gets angry about the effect of evil and a broken humanity and is devastated when we have to go through long periods of suffering. In his compassion, he acknowledges that our waiting has been long.

Even so, he does not just throw an opiate our way and hope it numbs the pain a little so we can stop annoying him with our cries. He sits with us and listens to our whole story and offers us the best of himself, which includes his power and his presence.

Jesus yearns not only for us to be free of suffering, but also that we might have relationship with him. And one does not take priority over the other. God does not trade our chance of healing for the sake of us becoming more eloquent in our prayer lives. We are foolish to walk with a sense of self-martyrdom, saying that we are destined to a life of torture so that we can become holier people. Instead, we must recognize that our healing and our relationship with God are tightly wrapped up with each other. We cannot have one without the other, because at the foundation of all our needs is a need to be deeply connected with the God who created us and loves us intimately. As much as we need rescue, we also need tangible comfort.

I walked into a doctor's office the other day with a list of typed bullet-pointed facts on my symptoms, assuming this doctor would be like all the others: giving me barely enough time to spit out a sentence before they rushed out the door to see their next patient. I handed my list to this doctor and she handed it right back to me without as much as glancing at it. "I want to hear it from your mouth. Tell me your story. I am here to listen." I told her my story for an hour and afterwards she gave me a big hug, saying, "You have been through so much. I am so sorry." And then she proceeded to give me medication that brought me significant relief. That was the best doctor appointment I have ever had.

God is the good doctor. He wants us to tell him our complaints and our dread of having to wait one more second to get relief. He is not going to rush off in order to make sure he has met his quota of patients for the day. He wants to spend time with us. He wants to hear our stories. He wants to let us sit and weep with him so that we can experience his embrace. He wants to give us his power and his presence. And that might just require a little more time than we originally anticipated.

God is thorough in his healing plan for us. He does not take shortcuts with our deliverance. The Israelites' exodus from slavery in Egypt and their forty years wandering in the wilderness is one of the most famous waiting periods in the Bible, and we can take great comfort in studying their journey. Exodus 13:17 says, "When Pharaoh let the people go, God did not lead them on the road through the Philistine country, **though that was shorter**. For God said, 'If they face war, they might change their minds and return to Egypt'" (emphasis added). God does not take shortcuts with us. He cares about us too much. He does not want to leave us in a cyclical pattern of affliction and will do anything it takes to help us walk in our freedom as his children, even if that means taking us on the longer road.

In the midst of the last seven years of pain, God has been proving to me how committed he is to getting rid of the power of fear in my life. Ever since my dad, who gave me a huge sense of safety, passed away suddenly when I was nineteen, I have lived in paranoia and anxiety that I have to somehow hold my world together or it will crumble when I am least expecting it. While I do not believe that God gave me this physical pain simply to teach me a lesson, he has most certainly been using it to continually invite me to trade that fear for trust. When my back pain first began, prayer ministers came up to me and heard God saying, "You don't have to be the keeper of your life. Let me be your dad." When my mouth flared up in pain right before my wedding, another prayer minister heard God saying, "Kelly, you don't have to be the keeper of your life. Let your heavenly dad throw you a party." When my feet began to burn with neuropathy and I plunged into trying to find a doctor to help me, I heard God say once again, "Kelly, you don't have to be the keeper of your life. Let me be your doctor."

I do not know when God will take this pain away, but I do know that as I wait, he will not give up his persistent invitation to trust him with my life. God will take every opportunity, and as long as it takes, because he knows that a trusting relationship with the Good Doctor is what will ultimately bring us the healing and comfort that we need.

It is in the waiting that we learn to surrender control of our lives. It is in the waiting that we learn to trust. It is in the waiting that we become self aware of our fears, desires, and our need for God. It is in the waiting that we get in touch with our desperation and learn to cry out for help. It is in the waiting that our hearts begin to beat with the saints who have gone before us. It is in the waiting that we get to know the God who suffers alongside us.

But we can choose how we receive that invitation. Neither Naaman nor the Israelites received the invitation well. Naaman chose to storm away in bitter rage, rejecting the opportunity for healing altogether, until his servants gave him a kick in the pants to talk sense into him. The Israelites saw God's provision in the wilderness over and over and over again, and still responded with complaining and bitterness. They did not do well with waiting.

Whether we like it or not, we cannot control when we will be hit with seasons that require longer wait times. But we can decide whether or not we will wait well.

How do we wait well? How do we take up the invitation

to get to know ourselves and the God who loves us deeply, when we find ourselves in the waiting room?

Here are some practices that can help us wait well:

WAIT BY ASKING FOR GOD'S COMFORT DAILY

When the Israelites wandered in the wilderness, God provided for them on a daily basis. He rained bread, or "manna", down from the sky to give them food to eat. But he purposely told them to collect only what they needed for that day and not store up more for the rest of the week. He wanted them to trust him anew every single day.

Chronic pain can teach you like nothing else just how much you cannot live on the bread of yesterday. You may feel wonderfully loved by God on Monday but then you wake up with new pain on Tuesday and you need him to comfort you all over again.

When we find ourselves in the waiting room, we have to learn to ask for God's comfort on a daily basis. We may find it easy to pray for *relief* on a daily basis (or perhaps you find yourself praying for that every minute of the day), but do we also pray for God's *comfort*?

Jesus desperately wants to have relationship with you. He wants you to pour your heart out to him. He wants to comfort you in a new way today than he did yesterday. One scripture verse will not be enough to tide you over. Five minutes of telling God you fears will not be enough release to carry you through the week.

Practice waking up each morning and telling Jesus how you are feeling. Tell him your fears, your dreams and your desires. Imagine him right there with you and ask him to comfort you once again. Let him shower you with stories from the Bible, hugs from friends, the assurance of his presence, new songs to sing over you. He wants to give you all these things and much more. Ask him, and expect his response. DAILY.

WAIT BY REFLECTING

Once we have asked Jesus for his comfort, we then need to learn to know how to recognize it. Often we do not even realize the ways Jesus has been with us or showing us something about himself until we pause to reflect on what has already occurred. It is in reflection that we often see God the most. St. Ignatius taught the valuable practice of the "Prayer of Examen" to reflect on the events and emotions of the day in order to recognize where God has been in his midst.

One way to practice the prayer of examen[11] is to review the events of your day and reflect on these three questions:

- Where did you sense God's presence or comfort today? Thank him.
- Where did you miss or betray God's presence today? Ask for forgiveness.

- What is one question you have for God? Ask and listen.

When we are in chronic pain, and we are trying to breathe long enough to get through the next moment, it can feel hard to pause and reflect. Perhaps we fear that our reflection on the longevity of pain will send us down deeper roads of depression and we would rather just focus on what is right in front of us. But it is in moments of reflection that we can see the signs of hope in our lives. It is in reflection that we begin to recognize God's persistent invitation to us to trust him, and it is in reflection that we begin to learn that he is worthy of that trust.

There are many ways to reflect:

- Try practicing the prayer of examen every night before you sleep.
- Make a timeline of your suffering and note the places where you have seen God meeting you.
- Ask your friends and leaders to reflect back to you how they have seen you grow during your season of pain.
- Ask God to show you what you have learned about yourself through your season of waiting. Are there ways he is wanting to make you more patient, humble, fearless and wise? How have you seen him

revealing the beautiful and broken parts of yourself as you have been waiting?

Do not stop at just reflecting on where you've seen God or how you are growing as a person. Thank God for what you notice. And then let your thankfulness move you into a place of worship and bring you hope that God will continue to be with you in the future.

One night I was particularly despairing about the seeming permanence of the burning pain in my mouth. I could not handle the thought of it lasting one more minute and yet I knew the journey was not going to be a short one. But then God invited me to reflect on my past. When my lower back pain first began, there was a good few months that I literally had no idea how to sit. I would lay face down on a couch while typing notes on my computer on the floor or go on walks and type sermons on my phone because I could not sit more than a few minutes before wanting to hyperventilate from the pain. But then I learned how to bring a cushion with me everywhere I went and, after years of physical therapy, sitting has become as easy as breathing to me again. The pain is not gone, but I can bear it a lot better. And as I reflected upon that memory, suddenly I had new courage to trust God with my mouth pain too. I stopped and thanked God for giving me relief from back pain that I never could have envisioned five years ago, and I was able to ask him with renewed faith to do the same with the current pain.

Reflection and gratitude are crucial to our lives with Jesus, and crucial to helping us get through the waiting room.

WAIT BY FIGHTING THE "NEVERS"

I remember being a kid and driving eighteen hours to Oregon every year with my family. Those were the longest car rides ever. I remember whining to my parents, "We are NEVER going to get there." To which they'd graciously respond, "We will get there. Listen to six more songs and then we will be at a rest stop."

Waiting can give us a serious case of the "nevers". *I will never get healed. I will never make it through this moment. I will never find a doctor. I will never get to do what I love. I will never be dependable again. I will never have a family. I will never get to achieve my dreams…*

About once a day my husband reminds me to stop saying that this pain will be forever. He tells me, "The only thing that is forever is your eternal joy with Jesus." This pain will one day end. Joy will come again. That is a fact. And whether you have been in pain for seven days or thirty-eight years, do not give into the "nevers".

Do whatever it takes to help you remember to fight the "nevers". Maybe it is listening to songs that will remind you of God's faithfulness and get you through the next half hour. Maybe it is asking a friend or family member to remind you on a regular basis. Maybe it is getting around other believers and asking them to share testimonies of how God has done the impossible for them. Maybe it is reading the stories in the Bible of Abraham, and Moses, and the bleeding woman, or creating artwork to depict those stories to help you remember that God is bigger than "never".

The doctor will come to see you. You are in the waiting room because you are expecting that he will. He will not leave you in the waiting room forever. Trust that he is the best doctor and that the waiting will be well worth it.

QUESTIONS FOR REFLECTION:

- *How do you feel about waiting? Imagine Jesus looking at you with compassion and acknowledging that your suffering has been for a long time. How does it bring you comfort to know that he sees it as a long time too?*
- *Reflect on a particular season of waiting (it can be current or past). What are some of the ways you have grown or seen God more clearly through that time of waiting? Thank him for those things.*
- *How have you spoken "never" over yourself? What helps you to fight that lie? Tell God that you no longer agree with that promise of "never" and affirm what you know to be true of him and his kingdom.*

Dreams

You wake me up
to desire them.
Reality threatening
all memory.

You unlock my legs
to find them.
Knowledge falsely
stabilizing.

You open my eyes
to see them.
Cynicism clouding
fulfillment.

You delight my heart
to gift them.
The originator rarely
remembered.

- Kelly Aalseth, 2016

Chapter 7

YOUR LIFE IS NOT OVER

I remember sitting in rush hour traffic one day, after another unsuccessful doctor appointment, and finding myself beginning to daydream: *What new plant can I get for our living room? What blog will I write next? Maybe I will take a dance class someday…* And I realized in that moment that it had been a long time since I had done any sort of dreaming for my life at all. The constant pain had brought with it an underlying depression that I hadn't even realized was preventing me from visioning for my future. Somewhere along the road of accepting that this pain was chronic, I had also unconsciously accepted the lie that my life was over. Not in a suicidal sort of way (though that is also a normal feeling when in chronic pain), but in a way that caused me to live dreamlessly, and with the assumption that my best days were over.

Dreaming is a gift. When we find ourselves dreaming, it means we are allowing ourselves to hope, and that hope comes from God. Learning to dream again is part of God's invitation to us to learn to get up and walk. When we have been crippled under the lies that say our best days are behind us and there is nothing meaningful that God may have in store for our lives, it is especially critical that we accept this invitation to dream.

I wonder when the paralyzed man at the pool (John 5:1-15), stopped dreaming. After year two? Year five? Year twenty-seven? When he saw the fifth person come out of the healing pool with their cure? The thirtieth? How many people would he have to watch get to see their dream realized while his life remained stale? How many unfulfilled hopes would he murmur before he just flat out gave up? Perhaps he had wise people telling him to stop dreaming. Thirty-eight years was evidence enough that his lot in life was never going to change. He would always just be that paralyzed guy who sat close to hope, but never close enough. He certainly did not have a thriving life ahead of him, let alone one of influence.

When I first started showing signs of chronic pain, caring people all around me told me that I should quit my job of ministering to college students. Perhaps my days of leading were over and I should just focus on my own healing. There was some truth to that. I did need a change of pace and I needed to learn a greater level of self-leadership and dependence on community. But I often was tempted to take that too far and think that I had to give up my dreams of leading altogether. In fact, that was not at all what God intended. As pain grew stronger, my influence widened. I got to be the director of one of the biggest college campus ministries in Los Angeles, see hundreds of students fall in love with Jesus for the first time, and work on writing national curriculum about racial justice. I frequently chuckle that as my capacity seems to become less and less, somehow my influence grows more and more.

That is what happens in the Kingdom of God. In God's kingdom it is the meek that inherit the earth. (Matthew 5:5). God chooses Abraham and Sarah, old and barren immigrants, to start his family line. (Genesis 17:17) God uses Joseph, the slave and prisoner, to save the Hebrew people in their years of famine. (Genesis 45:4-11) Jesus uses the woman who had five failed marriages to reach a whole village. (John 4: 1-42) God chooses the leper, the working class fishermen, the prostitutes, and the thieves to be heroes in his story. God writes his narrative of redemption through the very people who were told their lives were as good as over.

God is not finished with your life. He is the God who comes that you "may have life and have it to the full" (John 10:10). He is the God who gives babies to people on their deathbed. (Genesis 18:10-12) He is the God who breathes life into bones that have been dead for centuries. (Ezekiel 37:1-14) No matter how bad your life is now, no matter how many years you have been suffering, God still has life for you. And he wants you to dream for yourself in the way that he dreams for you. He longs for you to see your life not as one that is wasting away but one that is precious in his sight and worthy of living—a life that has purpose and, most importantly, a life that lives through the breath and heartbeat of God himself.

But dreaming is no flippant matter. One will not be able to dream easily again after years and years of failed attempts. Perhaps you have envisioned yourself married or with children, or going to med school, or starting a certain career, or being an athlete, or traveling the world...and your health or your circumstances have made it clear that your dream will never become realized. What are you to do? Does there ever come a point that you just need to stop trying?

I remember leading a conference once as a student and we were going to play a VHS cassette tape as part of our curriculum. The tape was not working and, in our incompetence in knowing how to use a VHS, we managed to pull all the tape out of the cassette so it looked like a spider web all over the table. My friend, who had not seen the tape yet, said in great faith, "It's ok! Lets just pray and it will start working again." I chuckled and showed him the tape that was now sprawling all over the floor and said, "I love your faith, but it is time for a new plan."

How do we know when it is time for a new dream and when we are to hope for the impossible? How do we know what to pray? God is the God who can cause the paralyzed to walk and can raise the dead to life, but he is also not so cruel to torture us by making us continuously dream for something that is not meant to be dreamt.

Dreaming is an art that must be learned. It is not as easy as the cute memes that say, "Just believe and all your dreams will come true." We can be one hundred percent confident that God has life ahead for us. But it takes skill to discern how God wants to grow and sometimes redirect our dreams. We must learn how to hear and interpret the words we hear from God and community about our dreams. And we must learn to feel safe enough in the arms of Jesus to tell him unreservedly about our hopes and our disappointments.

How do we begin to flex our atrophied muscles that have forgotten how to dream? How do we let God teach us to dream bigger dreams for our lives even when our bodies or circumstances tell us our best days are behind us?

GRIEVE LOST DREAMS IN ORDER TO EMBRACE NEW ONES

We cannot embrace new dreams until we've grieved the loss of the old ones. The book of Haggai depicts the criticality of grief as the Israelites are about to build a new temple. God says to them, "Who of you is left who saw this house in its former glory? How does it look to you now? Does it not seem to you like nothing?...The glory of this present house will be greater than the glory of the former house" (Haggai 2:3,9). God invited the Israelites to grieve their loss before he promised them something better. They had to acknowledge their despair in seeing the old temple in ruins before they could dream again for a more beautiful house of worship.

We often get paralyzed in knowing how to dream because we have not talked with God honestly yet about our disappointments. This may indeed be the hardest part of learning to dream.

The day chronic pain began for me was the day after I ran my second half-marathon. I had so many dreams that day of being a marathon runner like my dad and my brother. I had worked so hard. I was so disciplined in my training. But the very next day pain soared through my spine to the point that I have not been able to run since. I remember reading about someone else with fibromyalgia who decided it was time to throw away her race medals as a sign of moving forward. When I read that, I was devastated. I could not ever envision myself letting go of my dream of running.

I began to get honest with God. I told him I was not ready to give up my medals. Every time I saw someone jogging down the street, I whispered to God from my gutt, "It hurts." Eventually, God began to give me a new dream. I started to learn to swim. Just the other day I told my brother, "You know, I used to grieve so much that I could not continue to run. But I am realizing that I am actually a far better swimmer. I think I was made for the pool." I did get rid of my race medals eventually, but it was more out of annoyance for the space they took up than out of some kind of noble statement of moving on. I am not sure the pain of that loss will ever fully go away. I still tell God how it hurts when I see others jogging and I still hope for a day that I will run again, but I am also now able to fully embrace the joy of swimming, something I do not think I would be able to do without letting myself first be honest about my grief.

We cannot jump too quickly to new dreams. We must first be honest with God about our losses and our fears of letting go. We have to learn to tell him as often and for as long of a time as we need to that, "It hurts."

SURROUND YOURSELF WITH ROLE MODELS

It is easy to get stuck in the lie that our best days are over if we are surrounded by others who also believe that for themselves. Who we choose to put around us matters. The Psalmists knew the importance of remembering heroes of the faith and of recounting the ways God fulfilled dreams in the least expected ways. We are gifted with stories of past and current saints to look to as models, and as we see the most unlikely people live out their callings, our hope grows too.

I am so inspired when I hear the stories of students who are "Dreamers" who live under the threat of deportation, who are constantly put in the position of having to prove that they belong, though they are already made in the image of God. Yet they pour out their lives to lift up the voices of those who are silenced, while also giving themselves to their work and studies and caring for their families.

I look at the life of my grandmother, Eunice Eileen Joiner, who suffered for thirteen years from mysterious excruciating pain, later discovered to be interstitial cystitis. She spent each moment in pain talking with God and interceding for other people.

I look to my friend Rachel who has a learning disability and puts so much thought and time into sending me sweet notes, drawings, and stickers in the mail.

Each of these people and so many others have learned to live out their dreams and their callings on a daily basis even in the midst of great pain and loss. When we find ourselves forgetting how to dream, or wondering if God has any purpose for us still, it is often a sign that we need to surround ourselves with better role models. We need them to remind us that it is the hurting who get to usher in God's kingdom.

WORSHIP WITH WHATEVER YOU HAVE

When we face obstacles to living out our dreams, we often can feel like our lives are now a waste. We wonder why God would allow us to be smart and ambitious people who suddenly have no energy to do what we feel like we were made to do. *Why would God make me a strong leader and fill me with Kingdom desires and then not allow my body to carry out the plan? Such a waste!*

In Mark 14:1-9, there is a woman who comes to Jesus with an expensive alabaster jar of perfume, worth more than a years' wages, and pours it out onto Jesus feet. The religious leaders who see this, exclaim, "Why this waste…?" And Jesus replies, "She has done a beautiful thing to me... she did what she could."

We may have a million dreams of what we think we were made for. We may have hopes of becoming successful or impressing our families or of making change in the world. But what we are most designed to do, is to worship Jesus. This woman understood this. She did not have power or a name or a way to write books or give amazing speeches. But she gave what she could, and that was her worship. She worshiped Jesus with everything in her. And that is what Jesus honors, saying, "Truly I tell you, wherever the gospel is preached throughout the world, what she has done will also be told, in memory of her." (Mark 14:9)

Nothing is a waste if it is done in worship to Jesus. Whether you are bedridden, brokenhearted, feeling like your mind is not working anymore, or just simply feeling like you do not have direction for your life...worship. Worship with all that you can. Whether your offering means advocating for others who are treated unjustly, or simply sending a friend some cute stickers in the mail, do it with worship. Pour out your love and your life for Jesus and you will find your truest self come alive.

THE LESSON OF THE ORANGE TREE

As my physical therapist was working out knots in my calves the other day, hoping to relieve the pain in my feet caused by restricted nerves, he told me the story of his orange tree. He said that he was given a small orange tree and for seven years it did not grow at all. Every year he got excited about seeing the tree produce an orange, but then every year he would face disappointment. He had nearly given up on his dream of seeing his tree produce oranges, when he had a small thought: perhaps the decorative ribbon tied around it was restricting it from growing somehow. So he untied the ribbon, not really anticipating much result. He had to pull and yank on it to get it off, as the tree had started to grow around the ribbon. A year later, the tree had grown several feet and produced the fattest and juiciest orange he had ever tasted!

It is never too late for God to produce fruit in your life. Even if it has been seven years with no change, he is mindfully seeking to remove what is restricting you, and he will release you to live the life you were made for.

QUESTIONS FOR REFLECTION:

- *What failed dreams do you need to grieve and let go? Practice spending some time lamenting that disappointment with Jesus.*
- *What role models do you have that help you remember there can still be life in the midst of pain?*
- *What does it look like for you to worship in the midst of pain? Are there ways you can express your love for Jesus through your words, giving of your money, dance, song, or play? Ask Jesus to help you fulfill your purpose as you practice worshiping him.*

What a Friend we have in Jesus

What a friend we have in Jesus,
All our sins and griefs to bear!
What a privilege to carry
Everything to God in prayer!
O what peace we often forfeit,
O what needless pain we bear,
All because we do not carry
Everything to God in prayer!

Have we trials and temptations?
Is there trouble anywhere?
We should never be discouraged,
Take it to the Lord in prayer.
Can we find a friend so faithful
Who will all our sorrows share?
Jesus knows our every weakness,
Take it to the Lord in prayer.

Are we weak and heavy-laden,
Cumbered with a load of care?
Precious Savior, still our refuge—
Take it to the Lord in prayer;
Do thy friends despise, forsake thee?
Take it to the Lord in prayer;
In His arms He'll take and shield thee,
Thou wilt find a solace there.

- Joseph M. Scriven, 1855

Chapter 8

BECOMING A BETTER FRIEND

When chronic pain interrupts your life, it can be tempting to believe that you no longer have the ability to be a good friend to others. You may go from being dependable to suddenly dependent. You may find yourself spending long periods of time in isolation and unable to spend time with people like you did in the past. You may feel incapable of doing what you think a good partner, spouse, child, parent, or neighbor ought to do in order to show love to someone. Maybe you find your brain so focused on pain that you forget birthdays and anniversaries or have to bail on other special celebrations. Perhaps you feel like managing your health and your family life is enough and you do not know how to find energy to get to church and other community events.

While all of these circumstances may very much be your reality, it is a lie that pain has to rob you of your ability to be a good friend. In fact, pain has the potential to expand your capacity to love in really beautiful ways. Some of the wisest and most trustworthy of friends are those who have had their own share of suffering.

Becoming a good friend to others, though, is not a natural side effect of learning to endure through pain. There is nothing natural about real friendship at all, let alone loving someone when your own pain is exponential. Real friendship must be learned. It too requires us to supernaturally get up and walk.

In Mark 6:30-42, Jesus' disciples are exhausted from ministering to others. They are on their way to get some rest when a crowd of over five thousand people see Jesus leaving and run ahead to meet him. Jesus responds with compassion and spends the day teaching them. As it gets late, everyone is hungry and the disciples just want the crowd to go away so they can finally get some rest. But in the middle of their hunger and physical exhaustion, Jesus tells the disciples to feed the crowd.

Pain does not make us exempt from Jesus' invitation to show compassion towards others. His command to love our neighbor and to welcome the stranger is for all of us, even when all we can think about is our empty stomachs and our desire to collapse. Is Jesus cruel to ask this of us? Was he so focused on being compassionate to the crowds that he forgot to show compassion to the disciples?

Jesus does not ask the disciples to give more than they are capable of giving in order to wear them down further. He invites them to extend compassion on others so that they can participate in the joy of seeing Jesus as the provider. When they do say yes to Jesus' invitation to feed the crowd, albeit a bit grudgingly, they end up getting to participate in one of the greatest miracles. Jesus takes just five loaves of bread and two fish and multiplies it into the most lavish feast.

Jesus does not let our tiredness or our pain exclude us from the joy of participating with him in mission. When we take him up on his invitation to extend compassion to others even in the midst of our lack, we get to see Jesus show himself to us in ways we never thought imaginable. Jesus is not a task-master telling us to push harder. He is the miraculous provider who longs for us to be a part of his generous banquet.

Learning to join Jesus in extending compassion to others is not something that comes naturally to us. It must be learned. The disciples had no idea how to get past their tiredness and practice hospitality in an impossible way. They needed Jesus to walk them through step by step of what to do: *Go find what you have. Distribute it. Bring back the leftovers...*

We will not just automatically learn compassion for others simply because we ourselves are also suffering. We must look to Jesus and ask him to supernaturally open our eyes to others around us. We need him to show us how to love, perhaps in newer ways than we knew how to love before. We need him to show us how to translate what we are learning from our own pain into real empathy for others who may be really different from ourselves. We need him to provide miraculously when we feel like we have no energy left to love, so that we too can experience in his joy.

How do we let Jesus teach us how to expand our compassion towards others such that we can share in his joy?

INVEST IN YOUR FRIENDSHIP WITH JESUS

The more we get around Jesus, the more we will understand and experience real trust and friendship, and the more we will be able to extend that real friendship to others.

Just like every other friendship, sharing in real intimacy with Jesus does not come to us naturally. It requires time, investment, and creativity.

When I am wanting to grow my friendship with Jesus, I have a few art pieces that I regularly turn to. There are two old hymns called, "Tis so sweet to trust in Jesus" (Louisa M.R. Stead, 1882) and "What a friend we have in Jesus" (Joseph M. Scriven, 1855). The lyrics of those songs help me foster intimacy with Jesus. They remind me how trustworthy he is and how I can be free to tell him anything and everything.

There are also two visual art pieces that have helped me significantly. The first is a painting by Andrei Rublev called, "Holy Trinity" where the trinity is seated around a table with the cup symbolizing suffering.[12] They each look at each other with affection but also with sorrow. Rublev leaves an empty seat on the fourth side of the table, as an invitation for us to join the trinity and to share in suffering and fellowship with God. I frequently will gaze upon that image and remind myself when I am suffering that I am in great company. I use it as a starting point to talk with God about his suffering and how his heart is beating for me and for others in the moment.

The second visual art piece is by James He Qi and is a picture of the disciple Thomas leaning on the chest of Jesus as Jesus invites him to touch his scars.[13] It is an intimate depiction of Thomas' relationship with Jesus, and Jesus' invitation to lean upon him in our fears and doubt. I gaze upon that image and then imagine myself leaning upon Jesus' chest, hearing his heartbeat and asking him, again, how he shares in suffering with me.

These may not be the same tools that work for you, but we all need to find ways to help us foster intimacy with Jesus. Whether it is gazing at art pieces, studying scriptures, journaling your thoughts, going on nature walks, listening to podcasts...do the things that help you experience Jesus' closeness. Invest in your friendship with him. Do not just assume it will happen automatically.

ASK JESUS TO EXPAND YOUR EMPATHY FOR OTHERS

I come from a white, majority-culture in the U.S., and therefore there are pains that my friends and students from minority cultures have that I will never be able to fully know or understand. Even so, God has used these seven years of chronic physical pain to exponentially expand my ability to love and learn cross-culturally. While I do not suggest ever trying to compare pain (it is never helpful to say to someone, "Oh I know what you are going through," because you don't), I have seen God using this physical chronic pain to grow my compassion for those who know chronic pain on a much deeper level due to centuries of racism and systemic injustice.

There was a time that I was leading a leadership team of eighty students at UCLA and the Latino students were feeling unseen in light of the recent and frequent conversations we were having about #BlackLivesMatter. They were feeling unseen because of the way President Trump was speaking about their people and families, but they also felt unseen by their own fellowship. I remember immediately feeling defensive, and told God, "I'm trying so hard to take care of everyone and I feel attacked for not leading well enough."

Then I stopped and asked God to make me more compassionate and to help me empathize when I would never know their experience. As I prayed, God connected the dots for me and reminded me that I knew what it was like to have invisible pain and to feel unseen. He softened my heart and helped me lead with compassion rather than a need to protect my image. Instead of being defensive or just ignoring their suffering, I invited the Latino student leaders to my house for dinner. I then intentionally gave them leadership over our entire next leaders' meeting, providing them an opportunity to share their pain in the fellowship and what made them feel invisible. Later a few of them told me that that meeting was one of their most redeeming moments of the year. Even as I reflect upon the victory of that moment, I continue to yearn for the day when Latino students are not dependent upon white people in power, like myself, to invite them to have a voice at the table. There is need for continued systemic change. The voices of the Latino community are not only critical to Kingdom leadership, but are precious to Jesus, and need to be heard.

I will never know what it is like to be Latino, but God used my own experience of chronic pain to open my eyes to the real suffering of students under my own leadership. God called me not only to a moment of empathy but to a life of advocacy for the unseen.

In 2014, when I started reading about the senseless deaths of Michael Brown, Eric Garner, Ezell Ford, John Crawford and far too many innocent black men at the hands of law enforcement, I felt paralyzed. I had so much fear of saying something ignorant that I did not want to say anything at all. I again stopped and asked God to help me through my paralysis and to learn how to extend compassion. As I prayed, I was reminded of what it was like when my own father passed away. People often said things that were not helpful, but I also had some friends who did not say anything at all to me, except maybe a sympathy note on Facebook. That hurt even more. God prompted me to not just post my thoughts on social media, but to actually go have real conversations with my black friends and to ask them how they were doing. I remember feeling really awkward in bringing it up with my friend Keyanna, even though we were best friends since seventh grade. But I was shocked by her response to me afterwards: "Kelly, I have been in so much grief. And yet, you are the first white person who has asked me how I am doing. Thank you."

I did not have much to offer Keyanna other than the acknowledgment of what might be causing her pain. But what felt so incidental marked a turning point for us and launched our friendship into a whole other layer of depth as we continue to share our lives together.

We may not ever know what it is like to live in someone else's shoes, and we should never pretend that we do, but when we ask Jesus to use our own understanding of pain to grow our empathy for others, he will teach us and he will help us experience real friendship.

People like Keyanna and the Latino students in our fellowship have continued to be people who I can go to for comfort and empathy in my own pain. They are people who experience chronic pain in far greater ways than I will ever know, and they have become invaluable to me in learning how to actively trust Jesus. I brought my two fish and five loaves and Jesus gave me a banquet of deep friendship.

Real friendship does not mean that you are available 24/7 or that you can be a superhero. Real friendship means asking Jesus to move you with compassion in the way that he is moved with compassion. Real friendship means letting God interpret your own experience of pain so that you can begin to recognize pain in others. Real friendship means having the courage to acknowledge that you see the unseen pain of others around you and to share with each other in your sufferings.

ASK JESUS TO EXPAND YOUR PRAYER LIFE

Another opportunity that chronic pain can bring us is the gift of time. Whether you find yourself having to cut down on work hours or lying awake at night in pain, the amount of unhurried time in your life can grow. And while that time is not the kind of time that one craves like a vacation (lying in pain awake at night is a terrible thing), it also can be a place that we learn to pray like we have never prayed before.

It is amazing to see how friendships can grow simply through prayer. I may have less capacity to go hang out with my friends, but when I have been lying awake at night praying for someone, the mutual joy we experience together when that prayer is answered cannot compare to all the quality time in the world. My friend Rocio asked me to pray for her sister who was trying to have a baby, and I prayed every night for her for quite some time. When she delivered her baby, Rocio and I rejoiced together almost as if it were our own child.

Since my trip to India when I was seventeen, I have prayed for the friends I met there regularly for fifteen years. Just the other night one of those friends was able to come over for dinner and even though we literally had not seen each other in fifteen years, we felt so connected. We rejoiced in how God was working there and they prayed for me and encouraged me in my own pain.

Prayer has a way of surpassing time and space. Even when we are not physically able to be with people, we can speak to God about others and it draws us closer. It also is the way that God moves us to remember the people who are on his heart and how he grows our compassion and longings for them.

Our friendships can only go as deep as our prayer lives. Why not take advantage of the current pain you suffer to begin to let God expand the way you pray for others?

Chronic pain does not disqualify us from participating in the joy of God's kingdom. It can be one of the greatest opportunities to share with the community of believers all across the world and, ultimately, to share in the sufferings of our God.

QUESTIONS FOR REFLECTION:

- How has Jesus already made you a better friend to others because of the pain you experience? Thank him for that.
- What is one new way that you can practice intimacy with Jesus? Maybe it is setting aside some time every day to focus solely on him. Maybe you want to reflect on an art piece and use that to help you pray. Maybe you want to learn friendship with Jesus by playing like a kid and doing something you enjoy, while noticing his presence with you. Commit to one thing and try doing it every day this week.
- Who is one hurting person for whom you want to be a better friend? Spend a few minutes every day praying for them. Send them a note telling them you are thinking of them.

A Good Day

My foot leaves the floor,
my arm swings high.
"Fly!" she says, "Fly!"
The downbeat wiping memory
of all weightiness.

No ordinary lunch,
as I put my dance shoes away:
Sweet potato fries,
pancakes and oat bars
today.

I open my journal
and words splash out,
like colors on a canvas:
some match, some don't —
those are the better ones

He picks me up,
my hand in his,
spins me around–
the Bachata reciting
the rhythm of the day.

We leave on a tram
to a candlelight dinner
near the house of Tom Sawyer
and Critter Country.
Kisses me under the fireworks

Tomorrow I will wake.
Pain will return.
"Too good to be true,"
you could say.

But no, it happened.
Today was a good day.
A good day.

- Kelly Aalseth, 2018

Chapter 9

REDEFINING A "GOOD LIFE"

Chronic pain and fear can often go hand in hand: fear of waking up to a bad day, fear of pain flares, fear of the unknown future, fear of rejection, fear of not being able to sleep, fear of financial trouble, fear of being judged... you name it. But at the heart of many of these fears is an overarching fear of missing out on the best of life. Something at the core of all of us wants to know that our lives are going to be satisfying. We want lives of significance and to feel like we are thriving. And we are terrified that pain will cheat us of our chance of having the good life that we once envisioned for ourselves.

Pain in itself can be reason enough to feel we are missing out on the fullness of life, but cultural assumptions compound this feeling even more. While it is right to lament the pain we face and to pray in faith for full healing, we also need to be careful not to fall into the trap of believing certain lies about what actually makes for a good life.

Here are four lies we must be careful to combat:

LIE #1: A GOOD LIFE IS A COMFORTABLE LIFE

Our culture uses comfort as a marketing tool all the time: Wear these jeans so you will be cute and comfortable. Spend twice as much and get two more inches of legroom on your flight. Put on three different types of moisturizer. Buy a bed that has the perfect temperature all night long. Watch this television show while eating ice cream so you can forget about all the pain in the world. The overall message: be comfortable and your life will be good.

Add chronic pain to the equation, and the probability of believing this lie becomes exponentially greater. Comfort is no longer just a nicely marketed addition to life; it can become central to survival.

I lay awake at four in the morning recently, unable to sleep because of some sort of skin irritation that caused my legs to itch intensely. I wracked my brain for ways to calm the itching, while also trying hard to ignore the burning sensation in the bottom of my feet and the throbbing in my back that have now become my new "normals". Trying to get comfortable can no longer be just an extracurricular activity for me. It is vital to my sleep and to my every day ability to function.

But even so, comfort is not the main ingredient to a satisfying life. When I think about the most satisfying or significant moments in my life so far—running my first half-marathon, inviting a friend to follow Jesus, engaging in cross-cultural friendships, getting married—none of them could be described as comfortable. In fact, all of these times were very uncomfortable

During my trip to India, I remember sitting in 110 degree heat and humidity, with swollen mosquito bites the size of my fists all over my body, in a room with faulty electricity where the fans turned off every ten minutes, with people who spoke a language I did not understand, eating food that was unfamiliar to me. There was nothing comfortable about that situation. And yet it was there that my eyes were opened to the love and miraculous power of Jesus. I witnessed ridiculous physical healings. I witnessed people giving their lives to Jesus when they knew full well that their families would be against them because of it. I witnessed rooms full of new believers who were being trained to start and pastor house churches. God used that very uncomfortable situation to radically transform my understanding of God, his church, and my calling to ministry.

Discomfort, especially painful discomfort, is no joke. And we should never hold back from crying out to God for relief. But discomfort does not get to dictate whether or not we have good lives. We cannot give it that much power. Jesus says he "comes that (we) may have life, and have it to the full" (John 10:10). Can you imagine him adding a disclaimer: "Oh, except for when they are uncomfortable"? He never does that. Instead, he acknowledges that we are following a God who "has no place to lay his head (Luke 9:58) and he sends us out like "sheep among wolves"

(Matthew 10:16).

God is absolutely merciful and hates it when we hurt so much. Pain cannot be simplified to being a direct result of our choosing to follow Jesus (sin and evil have much more to do with that), but Jesus does make it very clear that his promise of a full life has no dependence on comfortability. We must be careful, when we are rightfully and desperately trying to get comfortable, to not give into the lie that we are robbed of our chance at a satisfying life simply because of our pain.

LIE #2: A GOOD LIFE MEANS A PREDICTABLE FUTURE

Another lie that our culture tells us is that if we just can foresee what lies ahead of us, then we will be good. If we know that our bills will be paid, that we will meet that special someone, that we will make it into law school, have a stable retirement and check off everything on our bucket list, then our lives will be satisfying. If we could see how the next ten years of our lives would play out, then we could live anxiety-free lives and relax into the present.

When you are living in chronic pain, this jeopardization of enjoying the present by constant fear of the future becomes even more acute. Your life is not only unpredictable as you think about your ten year plan, but suddenly your life is unpredictable on a daily (if not hourly) basis too. You may have a really great day where you feel like you're thriving but then you overdo it and you are in bed the next two weeks. Or you may feel like your mental health is finally under control and then suddenly depression knocks you in the face all over again. So you find yourself constantly going on WebMD and typing in "how long for this to heal...," wasting more and more energy wondering what surprises tomorrow may bring.

But what we really long for, even more than some kind of sidekick fortune teller, is to regain some semblance of control. The less predictable our lives become, the less control we feel we have, and that is a terrifying feeling. So we spend what energy we have trying to systematize the chaos and mystery in ways that make sense to us.

Nothing about Jesus' life was predictable. He never healed the same way twice. He was always open to interruption. There was never a day that looked exactly the same as it did before. Why? Because Jesus was not afraid to surrender control of his life (that was rightfully his) to his Father. He did not do things just because he would see them work well the day before. He daily asked his Father for direction and did what he said to do. And in doing so, his life was far more adventurous and meaningful than anyone else's in all of history.

While learning discipline and finding life-giving rhythms is a crucial part of thriving through chronic pain, we must be careful not to give into the lie that being able to predict how each day will go so that we can feel in control of our lives is what will make us happy. When we give control over to the one who is the best at managing our lives and ask him to teach us what is good, it is only then that we stop worrying about tomorrow and can actually begin to live.

LIE #3: A GOOD LIFE IS FREE OF LONELINESS

One of the most common experiences for those of us living in chronic pain is the feeling of loneliness. Whether pain causes physical isolation from community or an emotional isolation, loneliness is real. Small things can contribute to this sense of loneliness too. Not being able to eat the same food that others are eating at a party, having to use a wheelchair or other aids, not being included in relevant topics of conversation...so many things can make the sense of isolation even harder.

Our culture tells us that the solution to our loneliness is staying busy and connected all the time. We are constantly plugged into technology and get fearful and depressed the second we find ourselves alone in our thoughts. We cannot even use the bathroom anymore without pulling out our cell phones to make sure we are connected to others. And yet, we are a more lonely people than ever.

But it is not loneliness itself that makes our lives unsatisfying. It is our fear, paralysis and misguided assumptions about solutions to loneliness that can make our lives miserable. Choosing to embrace our loneliness can be one of the most powerful ways to experience God, but we have not yet learned how to maximize its potential.

Henri Nouwen, a Catholic priest who faced a distinct type of loneliness by choosing to live with people with mental disabilities, makes the case that, instead of trying to run from our pain of loneliness, we must actively work to make our loneliness beneficial. He says, "To live a spiritual life we must first find the courage to enter into the desert of our loneliness and to change it by gentle and persistent efforts into a garden of solitude…(this) is the movement from the restless senses to the restful spirit, from the outward-reaching cravings to the inward-reaching search, from the fearful clinging to the fearless play."[14]

Loneliness is not to be taken lightly. It is one of the most painful forms of human suffering and is worthy of our lament. And yet it too does not get to rob us of the full and abundant life that God promises us. Rather than dreading loneliness or simply sitting in pity for ourselves for having to face it, we can ask Jesus to teach us the art of turning the loneliness into rich times of solitude with our Father. And if we are willing to stay with him there a little while, we may begin to discover that the loneliness we once feared has turned into an invaluable gift.

LIE #4: A GOOD LIFE IS WHAT OTHERS HAVE.

Lastly, we must not give into the lie that says our lives are only profitable if no one else is making higher life gains. When we are facing pain, it is very easy to look at others who appear healthy and to then conclude that our lives are less than par. But Jesus is not interested in our comparison games. He does not operate with a capitalistic get-ahead-of-the-other value system.

When Jesus gets finished telling Peter about the brutal life of pain and death that he will face as he follows Jesus, Peter looks at his friend and asks Jesus, "What about him?" Jesus replies: "If I want him to remain alive until I return, what is that to you? You must follow me" (John 21:21-22).

What will give us the most satisfying life? Following Jesus. Not a pain-free life. Not a predictable life. Not a life that far outshines all our friends. The only thing that will give us the satisfying life that we long for is by following Jesus every day of our lives.

We can take comfort in the story of the Samaritan woman. (John 4:1-42) She lives in the chronic pain of the consequences of her past. Her reputation as a woman who has had five failed marriages causes her to predictably go get her water from the well every day at noon, the hottest part of the day, where she knows no one else will be. She is in constant pain and completely isolated from her community. But it is in this place, in her lonely, painful, routined life, that Jesus meets with her face to face and launches her into a life of significance. He tells her "Everyone who drinks this water will be thirsty again, but whoever drinks the water I give them will never thirst. Indeed, the water I give them will become in them a spring of water welling up to eternal life" (John 4:13-14). Her interaction with Jesus transforms her into a woman who no longer believes her life is void of value. She finds her reason to live and goes down in history as the one who transformed an entire village because of her testimony.

A good life is not one that is free of pain. A good life is one where we get to meet Jesus face to face in the middle of our pain and isolation and be transformed into people who are so confident of our value that we cannot help but lead the unpredictable life of making him known to everyone around us.

But how do we possibly remember these truths when we are in extreme pain? How do we, in the middle of the night when our bodies are screaming for relief, somehow believe that God has abundant life for us? We may know these truths intellectually but how do we translate them to our hearts when our minds cannot think of anything other than our pain?

Here are some practical tools to start:

MEMORIZE THE SCRIPTURES

We are inundated with these lies about what makes for a good life everywhere we go. We see them on our phones when we wake up, on billboards as we go to work, on the television in our homes. We hear them from coworkers and family members and neighbors. False messages about what makes a satisfying life are all around us. The only way to actively counteract these lies with truth is if we speak the truth over ourselves even more so.

God tells the Israelites to remember his words to them: "Fix these words of mine in your hearts and minds; tie them as symbols on your hands and bind them on your foreheads. Teach them to your children, talking about them when you sit at home and when you walk along the road, when you lie down and when you get up. Write them on the doorframes of your houses and on your gates" (Deuteronomy 11:18-20).

God is not being figurative here. Why not write the scripture on your door frames and hands, or on your computers and iphones? Why not speak aloud with your children the truths that you so desperately need to remember? Do whatever it takes to fill your mind with the truth of God and the lies will begin to quiet.

If you do not know where to start, try memorizing Psalm 23 or Psalm 121. Write them on post-it notes through your house or hang them on your fridge. Memorize another line each day so you can eventually practice reciting them as you fall asleep.

PRACTICE "WELCOMING PRAYER"

Mary Mrozowski, one of the founders of Contemplative Outreach, outlined a way to pray that has been very helpful to me in trying to combat some of these fears and false narratives in my life. Here are the basic steps of this "welcoming prayer" according to a contemplative activism site:[15]

- "**Focus**, feel and sink into the feelings, emotions, thoughts, sensations and commentaries in your body."
- "**Welcome** God in the feelings, emotions, thoughts, commentaries or sensations in your body by saying, 'Welcome.'"
- "**Let go** by repeating the following sentences: 'I let go of the desire for security, affection, control. I let go of the desire to change this feeling/sensation.'"

This type of welcoming does not mean that we are accepting that a life of pain or loneliness is all God has for us or that he cannot heal us, but it is a way of embracing the reality that even in our pain, God is up to something. Rather than running from our loneliness and discomfort and constantly fearing our lack of control, we can acknowledge the pain but also acknowledge God is with us in the midst of it. This type of prayer can help us to stop striving so hard to quickly "fix" our lives, but to begin believing that, even in the midst of our current reality, God has something good for us.

TAKE RISKS WITH JESUS

Lastly, we can combat the lie that a good life is one that is comfortable, safe, and predictable, by choosing to take risks with Jesus. Take up Jesus' invitation for a life of adventure. Share your pains and hopes with other people so they might know God too. Pray for things you think impossible. Extend love to someone even when you wonder if you have anything to offer. Ask the hard questions and relentlessly and curiously go to Jesus for the answers.

My drama teacher used to tell us when we were in the midst of doing back-to-back performances that the way to keep the show alive and fresh was by choosing one thing to do a little differently in each performance. Whether that meant making a face a little differently or walking with a little more bounce or saying a line with a slightly different cadence, those little risky changes made all the difference in making the show feel new every time.

You may not feel like you have much that is changeable in your life right now. Your health may depend on routine and the thought of an adventure may scare you more than inspire you. But there is always some way you can take a risk. Ask Jesus what risk he has for you each day and say yes to his invitations, and you will find yourself living the satisfying life you desire.

QUESTIONS FOR REFLECTION:

- *Which of the four lies above are you most tempted to believe? Spend some time rejecting that lie and affirming what is true.*
- *What risk is Jesus inviting you to try right now? Is it memorizing a scripture or practicing welcoming prayer? Has there been something you have been feeling convicted to do already but you have been scared to do? Commit to actually doing it with Jesus this week.*

Hope Unfulfilled

In the middle of the night
When all is quiet and still
I hear you begin to weep
I know the tears you'll spill

The pain is back again
It came rushing in at three
We don't know how or why
This complication came to be

I hold you in my arms
We both begin to pray
For your relief to come
Before the light of day

We ask and ask and ask
We hope and hope and hope
We don't have physical means
For how to deal and cope

I hear the lie inside you
That this will never go away
That hope unfulfilled
Is the only promise of the day

But please remember my love
I am right here with you
And that hopelessness inside
Is a promise that is untrue

- Michael Lee Aalseth, 2018

Chapter 10

THE HOPE MARATHON

The problem with hope in our culture is that we treat it like a sprint, when it is actually a marathon. We say things like: I hope I'm not late to work. I hope I'll pass my exam. I hope this person finds me attractive. I hope the Lakers win. I hope my family can all be home for the holidays. When in reality, these are not hopes at all (though they are all valid things to desire). They are wishes that will most likely come true in a matter of hours or months at the latest. Real hope is not so quickly resolved. Nor is it so easy to obtain. Real hope is something that must be learned through long seasons of training and practice. As the Apostle Paul says, "But hope that is seen is no hope at all. Who hopes for what they already have? But if we hope for what we do not yet have, we wait for it patiently" (Romans 8:24-25).

Chronic pain is one of the perfect training grounds for hope. It is through chronic pain that we get to learn to stretch our hope muscles such that they can endure the marathon and not just the sprint. But in order to do this, we have to stop believing that one, hope comes to us naturally and two, hope requires intensity at all times. We can be tempted to be like the person who never gets off the couch to exercise in the first place or we can train too hard. Neither one will help us run the marathon.

Sometimes being around people who are intensely filled with hope can be fatiguing. I remember being at an InterVarsity conference at Catalina Island where everyone around me was praying with so much genuine faith for revival and all I could think about was the pain traveling up and down my spine and my desire to go to bed. Another time a stranger heard that I was sick and immediately started praying for my healing by trying to dig up memories of my childhood that I was too exhausted to share about, and I came away feeling annoyed rather than loved. Constant intensity is not always what builds hope.

At the same time, we will never hope if we do not take the risk to stretch ourselves. At a similar student conference at Catalina Island, I heard the testimony of a neuroscientist and professor who had brain cancer and knew very well that he had only a few years to live. So he went around the world and asked every prayer minister he could find to pray for him. Whether they spoke in tongues, made him fall over backwards, or recited liturgy, he did not care. He said, "Either Jesus will heal me or I will die seeking his healing." He let down his ego and any assumptions of control and went to Jesus in every way he knew how. He never knew exactly which prayer session it was where he was healed, but fifteen years later he is still telling his story.

The preacher at this conference then talked about repentance and how that word literally means "to change one's mind." I realized in that moment that God was inviting me to change my mind about his ability to heal. I had built up this theology about how God uses suffering for good, and I was using that to mask my fatigue from being continually disappointed when I hoped for healing. And in that moment, I felt God stretching that hope muscle in me and convicting me that I had a long ways to go in having the kind of active faith this man had. Perhaps my 29-year-old theology of how and when God heals was not yet fully formed (shocking). God was inviting me to get up out of my tiredness and to start seeking again, and so I spent a couple hours with prayer ministers and felt God make significant breakthrough in freeing me from anxiety and panic attacks.

It can be tempting to look at both of my experiences at Catalina and to say that I had more hope the second time than I did the first. But that simply is not true. When I came back from the first Catalina conference and explained to my boyfriend (now husband) that I felt too tired to engage in the prayer meeting for revival, he looked at me with earnesty in his eyes and said, "Kelly, your presence is enough for God." My hope in that moment was not signified by intense activity. It was expressed by simply being.

Growing in hope requires both moments of rest and driveness. You cannot train for a marathon by running every single day. Some days you run five miles. Some days you run twenty. And others you do nothing at all.

Every part is critical to being able to endure through the marathon. Some days you may feel ready to be like that neuroscientist and ask a million people to pray for you because you know God is a healer. Other days you feel like all you can do is lay down and whisper, "Help." And in the moments of rest and of activity, God does the work to strengthen you so you can endure for the long haul.

There are times that having hope means getting up from our defeat and starting to walk like the man at the pool of Bethesda, but there are also times that having hope means allowing our friends to carry us through a hole in a roof to get to Jesus. When we are in it for the long haul, sometimes there are days that we need to actively seek out the testimonies of others and read the scriptures to fuel our hope. Other days we need the faith of others to carry us for a little while so we can just be still. Both the activity and the rest are crucial to our training.

Here are a few ways that we can choose to run the Hope Marathon rather than treating it like a sprint:

ASK JESUS HOW TO HOPE AND PRAY

This may seem so simple, but we often ignore this step. Jesus' ultimate desire for each of us and for this world is for relationship with himself which leads to our full physical, emotional, and spiritual healing, so we can never go wrong in praying for those things. However, there is mystery and perspective that we will never have without Jesus revealing it to us first. He is the only one who knows exactly what he is doing and what we ought to pray for. He alone has the ability to direct our hopes and our prayers such that our hoping is more effective.

Francis MacNutt says it well, "My faith is in God—not in my faith... Because of his wisdom, which so far surpasses mine, I trust that he understands, even when I do not, every motive, every circumstance involved in praying for healing...Because of my ignorance I sometimes pray for a mistaken thing, or in a mistaken way, and so I do not see the results turn out as I think they should. But these will turn out as God in his wisdom sees best."[16]

If our faith is in God and not in our own faith, then we can let go of the pressure of having to muster up hope that is not there or to pray in the ways we see others pray. Our role is simply to ask Jesus how he would have us pray and then to tell him the desires of our hearts.

There may be days where you find yourself regularly praying for physical healing and there may be days where you find yourself praying for the ability to let go of trying to grasp for control as pain abounds. Both of those answered prayers may feel like miracles to you. Neither is void of hope. They are just prayers that are directed in slightly different ways.

Romans 8:26-27 says, "We do not know what we ought

to pray for, but the Spirit himself intercedes for us through wordless groans. And he who searches our hearts knows the mind of the Spirit, because the Spirit intercedes for God's people in accordance with the will of God."

Ask Jesus what to pray for. Ask him when it is a season to rest and when it is a season to take action in your hoping. He will show you what is best.

ALLOW YOURSELF TO BE CARRIED BY THE FAITH OF OTHERS, BUT NOT TRAMPLED BY IT

As my Catalina stories demonstrate, there are times that the faith of other people can really help us and then there are times that we just are not ready to be prayed for in the way they want to pray.

You and the Holy Spirit inside of you get the most authority over your life. It is just fine to say to someone, "You know, I would love your prayer, but what I really need right now is to go to bed. Can you pray for me from afar for now and we can pray together when I have more energy?" Or to say, "I love that you want to pray for healing for me, but that's not quite the way I am feeling God leading me to pray right now. Would you instead pray for this…?" There is nothing unholy or unhopeful about these things. It is perfectly ok and often needed to tell someone what you are hearing from Jesus and what you feel your real needs are in the moment.

On the other hand, we also need to become people who allow ourselves to be carried by the hope of others. There are many times that I feel the hopelessness dwelling up inside of me and I need to turn to my husband or call up some of my friends and be honest with them: "I am losing hope today. Would you carry me to Jesus like the friends of that paralyzed man, because I don't know if I can get to him on my own."

In the same way that I may need to ask my friends for practical help, I also need to ask them to have hope on my behalf. Sometimes that means they pray from afar and I can trust their prayers to carry me. Sometimes that means letting them speak hope over me by sharing testimonies of God's power and reminding me of the promises in scripture.

We have to let ourselves be carried if we want to grow in having hope. And that always requires vulnerability. Sometimes it is the vulnerability to say we cannot find Jesus on our own, and sometimes it is the vulnerability to say that we want to be carried in a certain way. Either way, practicing this kind of honesty with others will help us persevere in the long run.

LET THE HOPE OF THE RESURRECTION BE THE UNDERCURRENT TO ALL OTHER HOPES

While there may be times that Jesus invites us to hope for a certain type of healing and that can be nuanced depending on the season he has us in, there is one hope that will never change or be taken aways from us. That is the hope of Jesus' resurrection.

It is because of Jesus' resurrection that we know our suffering will one day end forever. It is because of Jesus' resurrection that we know not even death itself can take us away from God's love. It is because of Jesus' resurrection that any hope that has died within us can be given new life day after day.

It is because of Jesus' resurrection that the apostles were brave enough to face prison, crucifixion and other torturous persecutions, because they were convinced that Jesus was King. And if Jesus—the one who created us and loves us more deeply than we could ever imagine—is King, then surely there is hope for us.

Romans 8:34-39 says:

> *Christ Jesus who died—more than that, who was raised to life—is at the right hand of God and is also interceding for us. Who shall separate us from the love of Christ? Shall trouble or hardship or persecution or famine or nakedness or danger or sword?...No, in all these things we are more than conquerors through him who loved us. For I am convinced that neither death nor life, neither angels nor demons, neither the present nor the future, nor any powers, neither height nor depth, nor anything*

else in all creation, will be able to separate us from the love of God that is in Christ Jesus our Lord.

Nothing can separate us from his love. Not chronic pain, not a lack of sleep, not depression or loneliness or even hopelessness itself. Jesus who conquered death can conquer all the hardship in your life. Because he loves you. And he is the resurrected King.

So ask Jesus how to pray. Ask your friends to help you find Jesus. Get up and walk while letting yourself be carried. But do it all while remembering the greatest hope of all: that the God who loves you has resurrected from the dead.

QUESTIONS FOR REFLECTION:

- *How is it helpful to view hope as a marathon and not a sprint? How can you extend more grace to yourself when you are not feeling full of faith?*
- *How is Jesus inviting you to pray in this season in regards to chronic pain? Is he inviting you to pray for healing or to pray for something else? Ask him to give you peace and courage to pray in that way.*
- *Spend some time reflecting on the hope of the resurrection. Let the reality of that sink in. How does knowing Jesus rose from the dead bring hope to your current situation?*

The Way

Look at all the people who surround you
Don't you see that no one gives a damn
Imagine everything that your life could be
Just accept that you'll never have the chance.

Arise from hopelessness
Stand up! Cast off the bitterness
Start walking, you will find yourself along the way

I can see them
Everyone around me
But they don't see me
I just feel alone
I've seen my hopes and wave them all goodbye
Because right now
I just need to survive.

Arise from hopelessness
Stand up cast off the bitterness
Start walking, I know you'll be found along the way.

- Michael Kim-Eubanks, 2009

Chapter 11

A WORD TO CAREGIVERS

Perhaps you have picked up this book because someone you love is suffering through chronic pain and you want to know how to care for them better. Or maybe you have read chapter 2, "The art of asking for help," and you wish to know a few more ways to help others know how to help you. Either way, this chapter is for you.

The best way to learn how to care for others is by looking at the master caregiver: Jesus. As we read the stories of Jesus in the Bible, our natural inclination can be to put ourselves in the shoes of those who receive from Jesus, but we are wise to also draw out lessons from Jesus' model of care for people. If we watch how Jesus cares uniquely and compassionately for each person he encounters, we can gain a treasure trove of lessons about how to care for others.

Look at the story of the paralyzed man at the pool again. (John 5:1-15) But this time, look for what we learn about how to care for someone who has been in pain for a very long time.

As Jesus interacts with the man at the pool, he does three things:

JESUS ASKS THE RIGHT QUESTIONS

Before giving any advice, or doing anything

extraordinary, Jesus asks the man a question: "Do you want to get well?" (John 5:6). We know by the man's response that this was the exact question he needed to hear in this moment, because it unlocked his deepest hurt. The question prompted him to safely share about his fatigue of having no access to healing, his loneliness of having no one to help him, and his doubt that anything could ever change. And it was this kind of honest conversation with Jesus that gave the man enough trust and courage to later follow Jesus' command to get up and walk.

The right questions are the ones that help us get honest with Jesus. The right questions help us unlock our deepest longings, fears, and disappointments. Not every question is right for everybody. Jesus rarely asked the same question twice, but he was a master of getting people to open up to him and to ultimately put their trust in him. Martin B. Copenhaver writes, "Jesus prefers to ask questions rather than to provide direct answers. Jesus chooses to ask a question 307 times in the gospel accounts. Even if Jesus gives direct answers to as many as 8 questions, that still means that Jesus is almost 40 times more likely to ask a question than he is to give a direct answer."[17] Jesus knew the healing power of questions.

So what kind of question can you ask of someone in chronic pain? A great place to start is: "What kinds of questions are helpful or unhelpful for you as you face this pain?" Many people will already have some ideas about what helps them simply from experience (and if you are in pain yourself, start generating your list of questions to share with others), but here is my list just to get the juices flowing:

Helpful Questions My Friends Ask Me:

- What part is most hurting/ frustrating today?
- Is it helpful to talk about your pain right now?
- How have you seen/felt/heard Jesus with you today? How has it been hard to find him?
- What is something you have been learning about?
- What has been helpful or frustrating about recent doctors appointments?
- Are you holding onto a particular word or scripture?
- What can I take off your plate today?
- What are you worried about the most right now?
- What will help you get your mind off things? What fun thing can we do together?
- What are you asking God for? Can I pray that alongside you?
- Do you want to pray together right now?
- Is it ok to pray for healing?
- What happens for you when you have a flare of pain? Are there similarities that occur or is it different every time?
- What is giving you joy right now? What things

beyond pain are you thinking about these days?
- What do you think Jesus would want to say to you right now in the midst of the pain you just expressed?
- Is there a lie that you are holding on to?

Even if you feel weird asking, or if it comes out a little funny, most people will feel loved simply by the fact you are asking them a question and wanting to be a part of their lives. But, on the occasion that you catch them in a moment where they do not want to talk about it, don't worry! Ask them if it is ok to ask again at a better time and express that you care. That will go a long way.

JESUS EMPOWERS

Jesus asks the man a question, hears his story, and then he empowers him by saying, "Get up! Take up your mat and walk" (John 5:8). Do not go around to every hurting person and say, "Get better already!" That will not go over so well. But what Jesus is doing here, is empowering the man out of the hopelessness he just expressed. He is responding to what he has heard from the man's story.

Empowering others who are in chronic pain can feel like a fine line to walk. You do not want to tell someone to do something that they realistically can not do so as just to deflate them even further. But you also have a powerful ability to bring faith when they feel they have none left. This is why asking questions first is so important. Empowe must flow out of our awareness of what the person is experiencing and hearing from God already.

I had a recent conversation with my girlfriends about my fears in thinking about starting a family. I told them honestly that I felt really scared of having kids, given the chronic pain I experience. But rather than telling me flippantly that I of course can do it (for chronic pain is a reality I can't not take into consideration), or that my husband and I are foolish to even try, they asked me some deeper questions about my past, present and future: How has God given you confidence and courage to do things before that you once thought impossible to do? How is God speaking to you currently about your desires and fears? What do you feel like you need to build your confidence for the future?

My friends heard my fears and helped me reflect deeper. Through their help, I felt God growing my confidence and helping me to ask discernment questions grounded in a reality of who Jesus has proved himself to be, rather than out of fear. This is real empowerment.

JESUS FOLLOWS UP

Jesus asks the right question, empowers him to walk, but then he follows up with him. He finds the man at the temple, confused and wondering what just happened to ıd interprets his experience for him and gives him ction for what is next: “See, you are well again. Stop ıning or something worse may happen to you” (John 5:14).

Jesus is thorough and aware that healing rarely just happens in a moment. He is committed to seeing people through their whole journey. He knows the importance of following up. Even just a little check in can make the world of difference in making people feel loved and well.

It is not enough that we ask someone how they are doing and take a moment to pray for them. We can take our love the extra mile by simply checking back in. *How was that prayer time for you? How have you been feeling since then? Now that you are through that flare, what are some things you found helpful or unhelpful from me during that time as I cared for you? Are there things you are learning about yourself and your needs that you want to identify for the future?*

The only thing Jesus did as much as ask questions, was debrief with his followers (which also involved question asking). His best conversations with his followers happened *after* some big event, crisis, or miracle. He took the time to ask them about their experiences, thoughts and emotions and helped them interpret what they were learning about God’s character and plan. More often than not it was during the times of reflection and debrief that the disciples began to recognize God’s presence in the midst of pain and crisis.

I remember discussing travel with my mentor and supervisor in InterVarsity. In a season of back-to-back conferences, he suggested that I go to one conference but not another with the intention of learning what works for my health and how I feel when I go and don't go to things. Instead of leaving the conversation at that, he then came back around to it when the two conferences were over. *How did it feel for you when you didn't go? What did you miss and how did it hurt your work and joy? How was it when you did go? Did the benefit feel worth the cost? What do you think God is revealing to you about traveling?*

I am so grateful for my supervisors, family, and friends, that help me to reflect. I feel so loved when they remember to come back around to things and are committed to walking with me for the long haul rather than just the moment.

Debrief is not only important for those in chronic pain. Caregivers and friends need the space and freedom to debrief as well. One of the most loving things a close friend said to me recently was, "I'm on your team and I'm not going anywhere, but I can also feel some fatigue when you have flare ups. It's hard for me when I feel powerless to help, and sometimes it's hard for me to get a read on what your pain actually feels like. Can we talk about the last major flare up you had with mouth pain on your wedding day so when the next major life event happens we can be a little more prepared?"

My initial internal reaction to her question was fear: *I knew it. I am a burden on my friends. They're all going to leave me. I'm so hard to love...* But then I remembered the story of the man whose friends dug a hole in a roof to lower him down to Jesus. I cannot imagine them going through that and then thinking, "Oh that was a piece of cake." So I turned to my friend and said, "Of course you are feeling fatigue! You've been carrying me through this for seven years. I wouldn't assume any differently. Absolutely, let's talk about that ridiculous experience of pain leading up to my wedding." And we continued to offer each other valuable insights about how to be better friends to each other as we navigate crisis. Rather than distancing ourselves from each other because of fatigue in caring or fear of being a burden, our friendship was strengthened through our debrief and we have a renewed confidence that we can get through the next crisis that comes our way.

Caregivers need to be carried by Jesus too. Loving someone through chronic pain is an impossible task without Jesus. And when you choose to get up and walk alongside someone who is hurting, you also must choose to let yourself be carried along the way. You cannot do it on your own.

And for those of us who suffer with chronic pain, we must be willing to let down our ego and remember that those who carry us to Jesus will get fatigued, and that it is just fine. It does not mean we curl up in a ball and stop asking for help or become self-martyrs and assume we are never allowed to lament. If we want to grow into maturity and see our friendships strengthen, we must choose to humble ourselves and say yes to the invitations to debrief our experiences. We must recognize how we need to grow in the ways we ask for help and be vulnerable enough to share our specific needs with others.

We are in this together. We all need to be carried by Jesus. We all need to learn from him about how to love well through better questions, empowerment, and follow up. If we try to do it out of our own will power, we will crumble out of fatigue. Our compassion will wane eventually. But when we look to Jesus and ask him to teach us to walk, he will do it.

From someone who has been carried by a community that continually looks to Jesus for strength, I want to say thank you. Thank you for carrying me. Thank you for acknowledging your shortcomings and helping me face my own. Thank you for having faith for me. Thank you for bringing me to Jesus and for teaching me to walk.

QUESTIONS FOR REFLECTION:

- *How do you need to be carried by Jesus as you carry your friends too?*
- *How does Jesus want to affirm you for your courage and perseverance in walking with someone through chronic pain?*
- *Is there something you need to debrief with a friend or family member about the way you have cared for them or the way you are receiving their care? Ask Jesus for courage and grace to have that conversation.*

Epilogue

JESUS WILL FIND YOU

Our family has a tradition of doing an egg hunt for the kids every Easter. My brothers and husband will go out and hide the eggs in really tricky spots so that our niece and nephew have to look carefully to find their treats. But this past Easter, my seven-year-old nephew and five-year-old niece handed the baskets to the men and said, "You're doing the finding this year!" and they proceeded to hide the eggs around the living room. It was hilarious to watch three fully grown men holding brightly colored Easter baskets and searching under couches.

When we are in chronic pain, it can feel like God is the dad who is hiding eggs from us hoping that we can figure out how to find them. We can feel like it is all on us to search for doctors, support groups, and solutions to the pain we face. We feel like it is up to us to figure out how to be spiritual enough to make sense of our suffering. We feel like it is up to us to find God.

And yet, God is the one who is looking to find us. He reverses the script and tells us that he gets to be the one to look ridiculous carrying the Easter basket and doing the searching.

The man who spent thirty eight years of his life sitting by the pool of Bethesda in bitter defeat, courageously decides to put his trust in Jesus and to respond to his invitation to get up and walk. And as he learns to stretch his muscles in ways he never thought possible, learning an entirely new way of life, Jesus *finds* him again (John 5:14). Jesus does not leave him to figure it all out on his own. He looks for him and teaches him how to keep walking.

Actively trusting Jesus with our pain is not just a one time decision. Learning to walk requires new risks every day. But Jesus will not ask you to courageously trust him and then abandon you to your own self-discipline or knowledge. It is not all on you to get it right. He will find you again and reveal himself to you so that your trust in him will keep growing.

Jesus is so committed to you. He longs for you to know him in a powerful and intimate way. He wants you to experience his love and healing in ways you never thought possible. He yearns for you to be able to trust him so much that you can lean all of your weight onto him and allow yourself to be carried.

Jesus will not stop pursuing you. He will woo you and challenge you and root for you until he has all of your trust. Jesus wants to find you. He wants to be the keeper of your life.

Endnotes

Introduction

1. Peter D. Hart Research Associate, "Americans Talk About Pain," Research America: An alliance for discoveries in health, http://www.researchamerica.org/sites/default/files/uploads/poll2003pain.pdf (Accessed Sept. 2, 2018).

2. Global Industry Analysts, Inc., "Global Pain Management Market to Reach US$60 Billion by 2015, According to a New Report by Global Industry Analysts, Inc.," Cision PRWeb, http://www.prweb.com/pdfdownload/8052240.pdf (Accessed Sept. 2, 2018).

3. Don L Goldenberg, MD, "Patient education: Fibromyalgia (Beyond the Basics)," Up To Date, https://www.uptodate.com/contents/fibromyalgia-beyond-the-basics (Accessed Sept. 2, 2018).

Chapter 1

4. Bill Hybels, Courageous Leadership (Grand Rapids: Zondervan, 2002), 182.

Chapter 3

5. Kobe Can, "Kobe Bryant Fight Matt Barnes," YouTube video, 1:05, Feb. 5, 2015, https://www.youtube.com/watch?v=4dGgL9PI3Cc

. Jimmy Kimmel, "YouTube Challenge - I Gave My Kids a Terrible Present," YouTube video, 5:09, Dec. 12, 2011, https://www.youtube.com/watch?v=q4a9CKgLprQ

Chapter 4

7. InterVarsity twentyonehundred, "John Ortberg 12/9 AM - Staff Conference 2014," Vimeo video, 37:31, January 2014, https://vimeo.com/83813282, (quote found in 11:23- 11:33).

8. Don Richard Riso, Enneagram Transformations: Releases and Affirmations for Healing your Personality Type (New York: Houghton Mifflin Harcourt, 1993).

Chapter 5

9. For more about listening prayer, see Dallas Willard, Hearing God: Developing a Conversational Relationship with God (Downers Grove, IL: InterVarsity Press, 1999).

Chapter 6

10. Joni Eareckson Tada, A Place of Healing: Wrestling with the Mysteries of Suffering, Pain, and God's Sovereignty (Colorado Springs, CO: David C. Cook, 2010), 99.

11. For more on Ignatian prayer, see "The Daily Examen," IgnatianSpirituality.com: A Service of Loyola Press, https://www.ignatianspirituality.com (accessed August 26, 2018).

Chapter 8

12. Andrei Rublev, The Trinity, 1411, Tempera, Tretyakov Gallery, Moscow, https://en.wikipedia.org/wiki/Trinity_(Andrei_Rublev).

13. James He Qi, The Doubt of St. Thomas, 2014, http://www.heqiart.com (accessed February 2018).

Chapter 9

14. Henri J.M. Nouwen, Reaching Out: The Three Movements of the Spiritual Life (New York, NY: Doubleday, 1975), 34.

15. Mary Mrozowski, "Welcoming Prayer," Gravity: A Center for Contemplative Activism, https://gravitycenter.com/practice/welcoming-prayer (accessed August 26, 2018).

Chapter 10

16. Francis MacNutt, Healing, (Indiana: Ava Maria Press, 1974), 94.

Chapter 11

17. Martin B. Copenhaver, Jesus is the Question: The 307 Questions Jesus Asked and the 3 He Answered (Nashville, TN: The United Methodist Publishing House, 2014), Introduction.

Appendix

SUGGESTIONS FOR FURTHER READING

Inspiration

Joni Eareckson Tada, A Place of Healing: Wrestling with the Mysteries of Suffering, Pain, and God's Sovereignty (Colorado Springs, CO: David C. Cook, 2010).

Steve and Sharol Hayner, Joy in the Journey: Finding Abundance in the Shadow of Death (Downers Grove, IL: InterVarsity Press, 2015).

Theology

Francis MacNutt, Healing, (Indiana: Ava Maria Press, 1974).

N.T. Wright, Surprised by Hope: Rethinking Heaven, the Resurrection, and the Mission of the Church (New York, NY: HarperCollins, 1989).

Poetry

A.W. Tozer, The Christian Book of Mystical Verse: A collection of Poems, Hymns, and Prayers for devotional reading (Chicago, IL: The Moody Bible Institute, 1963).

Prayer

Bill Hybels, The Power of a Whisper: Hearing God. Having the Guts to Respond (Grand Rapids, MI, 2010).

Paul E. Miller, A Praying Life: Connecting with God in a Distracting World (Colorado Springs, CO: NavPress, 2009).

Ruth Haley Barton, Sacred Rhythms: Arranging Our Lives for Spiritual Transformation (Downers Grove, IL: InterVarsity Press, 2006).

Loneliness and Isolation

Henri J.M. Nouwen, Reaching Out: The Three Movements of the Spiritual Life (New York, NY: Doubleday, 1975).

Shelly Trebesch, Isolation: A Place of Transformation in the Life of a Leader (Vista Group Consulting, 1997).

William Bridges, Transitions: Making Sense of Life's Changes (Cambridge, MA: Da Capo Press, 2004).

Made in the USA
San Bernardino, CA
10 October 2018